John Anthony's
Flora of Sutherland

John Anthony (foreground) together with left to right Professor
R. J. D. Graham, Professor Sir William Wright-Smith, Mr J. L. Smith
and Sir George Taylor

John Anthony's Flora of Sutherland

EDITED AND COMPILED BY
J. B. KENWORTHY

BOTANICAL SOCIETY OF EDINBURGH

© Botanical Society of Edinburgh 1976
Printed in Great Britain
at Aberdeen University Press

ISBN   0 903077 01 9

Contents

Editorial Note

John Anthony died in June 1972 at the age of 78 just at a time when his Flora of Sutherland was almost completed. His interest in the Scottish Flora was a long one stemming from student days in Edinburgh, where he read both arts and science. He completed his B.Sc. in 1926 and that same year he became a Fellow of the Botanical Society of Edinburgh. After some time in Malaya in the late 1920s he returned to Scotland as an assistant lecturer in Botany, first in Dundee then later as lecturer in Forest Botany in the University of Edinburgh. Retirement in 1958 was for John Anthony the stimulus to complete, what was for him both a challenge and a labour of love, the first county flora for Sutherland. He spent nearly twenty years of his life on this project, assisted for much of this time by his wife. I personally recall him as a quiet, modest yet friendly individual, whom I met from time to time in Bettyhill, the centre of his interests in Sutherland. A retired Army Captain from the First World War, holder of the Military Cross, a teacher, a scholar, an expert on wood anatomy, a man widely travelled in both the Far and Middle East and now the author of a county flora, such a combination of attributes is rare especially in our modern specialised way of life.

In compiling John Anthony's Flora, I have edited and added to sections he produced for the original manuscript. The sections concerned with Botanical Districts and Botanical Exploration are close to John Anthony's original, whereas the bibliography has been extended a good deal. Both the Index of Botanical Names and the Index of Latin Names have been added to the original script. I am particularly grateful to Mr Donald Paterson of the Botany Department of Aberdeen University for his help in this matter. I am responsible for the sections: The County of Sutherland, Climate, Geology, Soils, Vegetation and the Influence of Man. Dr Roy Watling kindly provided a short note on the Fungal Flora of Sutherland. Photographs are acknowledged individually. Throughout I have tried to blend my style with that of John Anthony. The main part of the flora has been edited and checked as far as possible and a list of authorities is to be found at end of the flora. In most cases the records are somewhat detailed being specific to the parish. While I have checked almost all the records with the Atlas of the British Flora, or with my personal experience of the north coast of Sutherland, I think there are very few doubtful records. In fact, I suspect that some of the older records may be confirmed and extended in the light of more extensive surveys especially in the west of the county. Thus any additional information or correction to the contents of the flora would be most appreciated.

I am indebted to Professor C. H. Gimingham for his comments upon the script and to Mr R. Mackecknie and Mr J. Grant Roger for similar services. I hope that the members of the Botanical Society of Edinburgh who have sponsored this flora will feel that they have made a positive contribution to Botany in Scotland with its publication.

Colour plates for a Flora are very expensive and I am grateful for the opportunity to use Shirley Poole's paintings. Permission to print the cover was given by Miss Shirley Poole of Middlesborough and by Misses Jean, Christine and Elsie McKay of Tigh-na-craig Bettyhill. The painting is one of many by Miss Poole to be found in several houses in Sutherland.

It took John Anthony a considerable time to compile his manuscript and it has taken me a number of years to produce the completed flora. During this time the Botanical Society of Edinburgh have shown immense patience and have always been in every way an encouragement.

J. B. Kenworthy
June 1976
University of Aberdeen

Acknowledgements

I wish to thank

Dr D. Radcliffe of the Nature Conservancy for lists of species mainly alpine from the Western Mountains

Mr D. McClintock for lists of species from Durness which he had compiled over a long period

Mr A. G. Kenneth of Ardrishaig for lists from the northwest which included new localities and species of *Hieracia*

Mr P. Sell who not only named but supplied a record of that genus in Sutherland

Mr J. Dandy who supplied a record of *Potomageton*

Dr Yeo who named all my gatherings of *Euphrasia*

Dr Edees who named the *Rubi*

Professor J. R. Matthews who named the *Rosa* species

Dr Ursula Duncan for her contribution of lists from some remote areas

I am grateful to Dr Perring and his staff at Monkswood for their constant interest in my researches

John Anthony
January 1972
Edinburgh

The County of Sutherland

From the North Sea to the Atlantic Ocean the far north of Scotland is an area quite unlike any other in Britain. Sutherland is a countryside apparently compressed by the sky into the great central plain of A'Mhoine, and a coastline torn to pieces by storm seas. A large county, the fifth largest in Scotland, it suffers from an overabundance of peat and rock. This empty landscape has hidden within it evidence of a time of trees and straths crowded with people. Now the population of Sutherland live in sheltered and fertile areas along the coast; isolated houses in scattered crofting communities.

The grandeur of the county is expressed in its extensive horizon. In many places a view of 20 miles is not uncommon. The north coast is formed of precipitous cliffs with only a few sandy beaches. From Cape Wrath to Strathy Point the cliffs are for the most part over 400 ft in height but reach 900 ft on Clo Mor. The two Kyles of Durness and Tongue, each with wide sands and set against a backcloth of high mountains, break this flat northern coastline. In contrast, Loch Eriboll with its fiord-like contours has an isolated beauty of its own and is at the same time one of the greatest natural harbours in Britain. Of the northern mountains, Ben Loyal and Ben Hope are the most outstanding, the former with its steep northern face and central castle dominating the countryside for a great distance around. Even Coldbackie Hill (the watch hill), although only 1000 ft, has imposing conglomerate cliffs rising almost vertically from the sea and commanding a view from the Hebrides to the Orkneys.

The eastern boundary with Caithness follows a watershed from Drumhollistan in the north to the Ord in the east. From Melvich to Kinbrace along Strath Halladale, the boundary is one of wild moorland and deer forest. Moving further south, Kinbrace is the gateway to the strath of Kildonan, where gold and semi-precious stones are found. Helmsdale, a fishing port of some repute in earlier times, lies at the southern end of the boundary with Caithness.

Along the south-east, bounded by the Moray Firth, is a low flat coastline fringed with sand dunes and one large inlet, the land-locked Loch Fleet. Further north, near Loth, another loch with its accompanying swamp was drained during the last century. In this area ample evidence of man's influence over some considerable time period can be found in the remains of brochs and chambered cairns on the flat coastal areas south of Loth. The south-east of the county from Brora to Bonar Bridge is the most densely populated area in the county, lying as it does on good soils derived

1

from friable sandstones and in an unexposed and warm climatic zone. Around Golspie these conditions result in good agricultural land and extensive woodlands.

On its southern boundary, the county is one of contrasts in scenery. From Bonar Bridge westwards up the Shin valley trees dominate the countryside; many of them planted along the Kyle of Sutherland by the Forestry Commission. The boundary then follows the course of the River Oykell, in its broad valley to a source on the slopes of Breabeg (2670 ft) and southwards along the watershed to the Cromalt Hills (1692 ft). The western end of the boundary enters the sea at Loch Kirkaig after traversing Loch Veyatie and Fionn Loch. As well as crossing a great range of geological structures from the new sandstones of the east to the very old Lewisian gneiss of the west, through Durness limestone at Elphin and Inchnadamph, the south of the county contains a wide range of plant habitats due to a variety of climatic conditions. The west coast and higher hills of central Sutherland are extremely exposed, while the east coast and Kyle of Sutherland are comparatively sheltered. The west coast of Scotland is renowned for its beauty although this is associated more with the counties of the south. However, the coastline of Sutherland has tremendous variety and beauty, from the cliffs of Stoer Head and the glorious white sands of Achmelvich to the mountains of Suilven, Cannisp and Quinag. Many sea lochs and bays along the west coast give a long, tortuous coastline which is, for the most part, rocky but with wide sandy bays at Sandwood, Scourie, Clashnessie, Stoer, Clachtoll and Achmelvich. Innumerable islands, of which Handa and Oldany are the largest lie off the coast; some are used for grazing but none are inhabited. The topography of this area is most important for plant life, since any place which affords shelter from the westerly winds can reap the benefit from a generally mild climate on the west coast. In the far north-west of the county lies the desolate and extremely exposed coastline of the Parphe, a highly inaccessible area of great beauty and interest. The Parphe was mentioned in Blaeu's Atlas as having many wolves and later Gordon cites the area as one with an abundance of red deer. The geological structure is one of Lewisian gneiss, covered by blanket peat, with scattered outcrops of sandstone and limestone while bare quartzite screes occur on Ben Stack and Foinaven.

In the interior, Sutherland is a vast plain of peat, broken only by the isolated mountain peaks of Ben Hope, Ben Loyal and Foinaven in the north; Ben Griam More, Ben Griam Beg, Ben Armine and Ben Klibreck in the centre and Ben Stack, Ben More Assynt and the trio of Cannisp, Quinag and Suilven in the west.

The county may be divided into three drainage basins. To the north the rivers drain into the Pentland Firth. These are the Dionard into the Kyle of Durness, the Hope from Loch Hope, the Borgie and the Naver into Torrisdale bay, the Strathy from Loch Strathy and the Halladale which enters the sea at Bighouse bay. To the west three large rivers flow into the

Atlantic Ocean; the Laxford from Loch Stack, the Inver from Loch Assynt and the Kirkaig from Loch Veyetie. In the third zone the rivers flow into the Moray Firth. These are the Helmsdale, Brora, Golspie, Fleet, Evelix and the Oykell with its tributaries the Cassley and the Shin. There is a very large number of lochs in the county, especially in the west, varying in size from Loch Shin (17 miles) to mere lochans. They provide an interesting and diverse habitat for aquatic plants, from the alkaline lochs of the limestone districts (also famed for their large trout) to the peaty and highly acid lochans scattered throughout the west and over the central plain.

Geology

A short section on the geomorphic pattern of the preglacial landscapes of Sutherland is included in this flora because in many cases the composition of these older rocks has a dominating control over soil formation within the county. Thus geological formations influence the distribution of vegetation types and individual species. The geology of Sutherland is as varied as anywhere in Europe although much of the variation is found in the extreme east and west of the county, the central belt being dominated by Moine Schists.

A most important feature of solid geology in Sutherland is the great Moine Thrust plane running SSW from Loch Eriboll, which separates the eastern Moine schists from the complex assemblage of Lewisian, Torridonian and Cambrian rocks of the west. The oldest rocks of the area are thought to be the Lewisian gneisses which form the basic rock structure of Sutherland. This structure was intensively folded and metamorphosed to give a denuded surface upon which the Torridonian sandstones were laid down during the Pre-Cambrian. Relict hills of sandstone are clearly seen overlying the Lewisian strata around Lochinver. Early geologists likened Suilven, Cannisp, Cul Mor and Cul Beag to Torridonian ships on a Lewisian sea and this description is most apt. The gneiss, with its numerous intrusive dykes of basalt, granite and basic rocks, is intensively ice-worn, giving rise to grey knolls and ridges, polished smooth and bare, which retain their comparative level except towards their eastern boundary where it rises steeply to form the western flanks of Cranstackie, Foinaven, Arkle and Ben Stack. Innumerable hollows have been scooped out by ancient glaciers and these now form hundreds of lochans, which with the large expanses of bare rock, are characteristic of this formation. In the extreme north, near Cape Wrath, Torridonian sandstones form magnificent sea cliffs at Clo Mor.

The Cambrian strata, including Durness limestone, overlie Torridonian sandstones. Mudstones, quartzites and grits are also included in this period. Quartzite forms a variable layer up to 500 ft thick in places, capping the sandstones on Foinaven in the south,. while forming the sea cliffs of Whiten Head in the north. This quartzite breaks up into sharp fragments resulting in large screes which characterise the landscape. Where quartzite predominates the land is barren and devoid of vegetation. In its upper surfaces this old sea bed is fine grained and compact and has, running at right angles, cylinders of the same material caused by the action of sand worms. This gives the name pipe-rock to the quartzite. Above the

Fig. 1 County of Sutherland. Place names mentioned in the text

5

pipe-rock is a band of brown calcareous shale, with thin dolomite beds and flaggy grits up to 50 ft thick which are traversed by dark markings, originally attributed to sea-weeds, and thus named fucoid beds. On weathering the shale produces a yellowish clay, which being lime-rich, has marked effects upon the accompanying vegetation. The upper layer of limestone is grey in colour and outcrops from Durness to Assynt. Cambrian limestones of the Durness area are the thickest in Scotland. They are extremely variable in quality, in some places containing large amounts of dolomite, while in others siliceous matter is dominant.

Millions of years later the great Caledonian earth movements forced a mass of older metamorphic rocks, the Moine series, westward over the Cambrian series until a narrow wedge of Cambrian rocks was left exposed to the west of the Moine Thrust plane. This process gave rise to the present geological framework of two areas of Pre-Cambrian rocks separated north to south by a band of Cambrian limestone.

The rocks of the Moine series are so called from their occurrence in A 'Mhoine, a tract of peaty moorland which extends east of the Moine Thrust. From a lithological point of view the Moinian rocks are as monotonous as the Lewisian are diversified. Highly siliceous, flaggy granulite is widely distributed within this series together with finer grained peltic rocks and bands with distorted pebbles from original conglomerates. The flattish areas at 900 to 1000 ft are the remains of planation surfaces with Ben Hee and Ben Klibreck as inselbergs (island mountains) of Pre-Cambrian rock rising from a Triassic desert. This wide tract of country, from Whiten Head to the Cromalt Hills, westward to Strath Halladale and Strath Ullie, is covered with deep peat forming rough moorland and bog.

From the Dornoch Firth to Helmsdale there lies a belt of Old Red Sandstone some five miles wide. Traces of this formation occur on the summit of Ben Armine and at Strathy and Tongue on the coast. Ben Griam More and Ben Griam Beg form terraced pyramids of conglomerate. Ben Loyal owes its distinctive outline to the massive crystalline syenite of which it is composed.

Between the Old Red Sandstone and the Moray Firth, from Golspie to Helmsdale, lies a narrow belt of the newer rocks forming successive layers of sandstone, shale and limestone. These rocks are overlaid with later glacial drifts and boulder clay. More recent still are the peat deposits and the areas of blown sand which form dunes at many places around the coast.

(*J. B. Kenworthy*)

Plate 1 **Sedum rosea** Roseroot

(*J. B. Kenworthy*)

Plate 2 **Carex rostrata** and **Equisetum fluviatale** Bottle Sedge and Water Horsetail

Soils

The complex nature of geological structures, extreme conditions for weathering and the glacial outwash process have led to a wide array of soil structures in Sutherland. Modification of these chemical and physical units has taken place since the last glaciation over a period of 10,000 to 15,000 years. High precipitation and low evaporation in northern climates results in a net downward movement of water. In addition, the influence of man in promoting grazing and burning has modified the vegetation thereby affecting soil development.

The soils of Sutherland are dominated by the products of older metamorphic rocks and are generally acid. The reasons are threefold; the soils are derived from a solid geology which is low in bases such as calcium and magnesium; the rocks are not weathered rapidly; and most of Sutherland is in an area in which movement of water in the soil is predominantly downward. Thus a situation arises that any plant nutrients which are released from rocks in the weathering process are quickly rendered unavailable to the vegetation. For large parts of Sutherland the main source of plant nutrition is rainwater.

In regions with outcrops of limestone, dolomite, calcareous schists, hornblende schists, calcareous sandstone etc., bases, mainly calcium and magnesium, derived from the easily weathered rock structures, replenish the soil with nutrients and ameliorate soil acidity.

In such areas the effects upon soil and vegetation are most marked. This feature is very striking all along the edge of the Moine thrust, but particularly easily viewed along the shores of Loch Eriboll between Kempie and Heilam, at Durness on the massive outcrops and further south at Inchnadamph. The contrast with more acid soils is apparent in the absence of undecomposed organic remains in these soils.

Much of the soil in Sutherland is made up from organic remains of plants accumulating under anaerobic, acid conditions. The major formation is blanket peat developed as a continuous layer of acid organic material, sometimes formed on bare rock but usually over a mineral skeletal soil – always in areas of high rainfall or high humidity. This layer varies in thickness from a few centimetres to over a metre. The upper part of the peat is made from undecomposed vegetation, usually composed of *Trichophorum caespitosum*, *Eriophorum* and *Sphagnum* spp. in the west, whereas on the east and north coasts *Calluna vulagaris* and *Erica* spp. are the contributory species. The former give a dark amorphous peat and the latter a browner fibrous peat. In the west this peat formation can often be

7

recognised from a distance as eroded hags with shining west faces made up from the moss *Rhacomitrium lanuginosum*.

In areas where the topography is gently undulating ground or a flat enclosed basin, water accumulates giving rise to deeper peat sometimes greater than 10 m in depth. Conditions of this type are found throughout Sutherland but predominate in the north and west, especially in the older gneiss landscape. This topogenic peat is made up entirely from plant remains reflecting in the vegetation layers the history of climatic change in the area since the last glaciation. Layer upon layer of partially decomposed plant remains show the beginnings of post-glacial vegetation with sedges and reeds passing through drier periods when trees invaded the area. Some of the tree stumps in this area, birch and pine, remain embedded in the peat. Birch stumps occur throughout a large depth of peat whereas pine stumps occur usually in one layer but some times as two distinct horizons. Above the tree stumps, dark peat formed from *Calluna* and *Eriophorum* is present, reflecting a cooler wetter climate. Finally the uppermost peat is mainly composed of *Sphagnum* spp.

Where glacial debris has been deposited in the straths of Sutherland or on rock surfaces with only a slight slope, soils have developed which show a structure involving three basic horizons. The mineral soil consists of an A horizon from which minerals and in some cases small particles have been removed; a B horizon into which minerals are deposited and a C horizon of unaltered parent materials. This is usually capped by organic debris in various stages of decay in which the name of the horizon describes the organic matter and its state of decay, litter, fermentation and humus.

A brown earth soil develops in association with herb rich vegetation, usually bearing birch forest in the north and east with oak in the west, or where trees have been removed, good agricultural grassland. Here the A and B horizons are indistinct and good mixing in the soil maintains a relatively even distribution of minerals within the soil, showing little signs of leaching.

If the underlying rocks are poor in minerals and soil develops in an area of high rainfall, above the tree line or where heather has been encouraged by grazing and burning, then a podsol of some type may result. Podsols are characterised by a leached A horizon from which the sesquioxides of iron and aluminium have been removed leaving an ash grey layer. These compounds, together with other nutrients, are deposited at a lower level within the soil giving either a red stained layer of soil, in the case of the iron podsol, or two layers red stained with iron and black stained with humus particles in an iron humus podsol. Throughout central and eastern Sutherland the thin iron pan podsol with a characteristic well defined layer of oxides, 20–30 cm below a cap of raw humus, is widespread. These soils are easily examined in roadside quarries on the A836 and the A897.

Richer soils are confined to straths in the north and east whereas the strong influence of Durness limestone is seen in the west. Rendzinas are soils which develop from highly calcareous parent material as shallow soils dark brown in colour and generally with a low clay content. They form a neutral mull-like humus. In Sutherland they support largely grassland and agricultural land having in general a great diversity of species, both higher plants and cryptogams. Rendzinas are found from Balnakiel in the north to Inchnadamph in the south.

On high ground in the east as in the west above 2000 ft the soils are thin and skeletal. These mountain tundra soils have poorly developed horizons caused by weak chemical or biological processes. Such soils are formed under very cold conditions and are composed of angular fragments. In patterned mountain tundra soils the fragments are frost sorted to form solifluction terraces usually bounded by vegetation (Crampton, 1912). The Hamada mountain tundra soils have a continuous layer of fragments with frost sorting absent.

Among the more infrequent soils, one is particularly important in the coastal vegetation of Sutherland. At Invernaver calcareous sands containing 2–4 per cent $CaCO_3$ are blown by coastal winds to a height of 400 ft above the beach. The calcium is derived from shell fragments in the sand. On this sand, which shows little development into horizons, except for banding caused by fresh additions of sand, *Dryas octopetala* is probably as abundant as anywhere in Britain. Where springs seep through the sand, calcareous flushes develop in which *Primula scotica* is to be found.

Climate

The climate of Sutherland shows a wide range of variability. A striking contrast exists between the wetter, milder, climate of the more exposed and rugged west coastal district and that of the drier eastern and northern shores. In the western coastal zone the prevailing winds during the winter and summer months are from the south-west. These bring abundant moisture from the Atlantic Ocean. Rain occurs on more than 200 days each year. The annual average rainfall is 150 cm (60 in.) while the mean annual temperature is 10°C (50°F). The lowlands on the Moray Firth coast lie in the dry belt of eastern Scotland; the average annual rainfall is 77 cm (31 in.). During the spring and early summer cold northerly and north-easterly winds prevail, often bringing sea-fog. The mean annual temperature is 6·2°C (45°F). A further difference is in the range of temperature. In the west the January mean is 6·2°C (45°F) and that of July 12·2°C (54°F). The comparative figures for the east are, January 3·3°C (38°F) and July 14°C (57°F). In the north coastal region, as in the east, cold northerly and north-easterly winds blow during the spring and early summer; the average rainfall is 90 cm (36 in.) and the mean annual temperature 6·2°C (45°F). In all coastal areas snow seldom lies long and the winters are comparatively mild for these latitudes. In the interior, however, the climate is more rigorous. The winters are long and severe, with snow persisting on the hills. Rainfall is high, especially in the western hills, Ben More Assynt 250 cm (100 in.), but declines towards the east. In all areas wind exerts a profound influence, often blowing at gale force, but precise data are not recorded. In these latitudes the amount of daylight differs widely between summer and winter. On the north coast daylight in June approximates 20 hours per day while in January there is scarcely 6 hours. The daily average amount of sunshine in summer is 3 hours and in winter 1 hour. Due to the low elevation of the sun many areas particularly in the valleys receive no sunlight during some of the winter months.

On the whole then, the summers have long daylight but winter days are short and in the autumn frosts come early affecting the valleys which are shaded from the sun by high hills. The winters are long, dark, dreary and boisterous.

Birse and Dry (1970) have assessed the climate of Scotland on the basis of accumulated temperature above 5·6°C and potential water deficit. Such parameters are thought to contribute to a major control of plant growth in terms of potential growing season and utilisation of available water.

Their classification produces approximately eighteen climatic sub-types of which fifteen are present in Sutherland. Of this wide range of sub-types, those described as 'warm' have accumulated temperatures of over 1375 day degrees and are absent from Sutherland, while others ranging through 'fairly warm' (1100–1375 day degrees) 'cool', 'cold', 'very cold', to 'extremely cold' (0–275 day degrees) are present. These units cover the range 'dry' to 'wet' and occur over a physiographic range from lowland to mountain. However, any assessment of climate for Sutherland suffers from a lack of information; the whole county map being based upon six weather stations.

A large part of Sutherland is classified as cool wet foothills and uplands, slightly drier in the east but still rather wet. A coastal zone of fairly warm moist lowland stretches around the west and north coasts in a band, which is never more than 5 miles wide. On the north coast it rapidly merges with a 'cool' zone whereas on the west coast the transition may take 10 or 20 miles and traverse warm but increasingly wetter zones.

Another climatic feature which dominates the Sutherland scene is exposure. In a second climatic map Birse and Dry (1970) have used exposure and accumulated frosts as a basis for their climatic regions. As the assessment of exposure is based largely upon changes in terrain and this is so variable in Sutherland, the picture produced is extremely complex. Most of Sutherland is classified as 'exposed', 'very exposed' or 'extremely exposed', having average wind speeds ranging from 4·4 m/s (8·9 m.p.h.) to greater than 8·9 m/s (18·0 m.p.h.). The only areas classified as sheltered are stretches of country around Bonar Bridge, Strath Oykel, west of Dornoch and a small area near Loch Brora. These have a mean windspeed below 2·6 m/s (5·85 m.p.h.).

The 'moderately exposed' region having wind speeds between 2·6 and 4·4 m/s is generally absent from the west coast but stretches inland along the straths of the east and north coasts. These areas represent the drainage pattern of the sloping Moine thrust which is normally N.W.–S.E. but is also cut to the north by Strathnaver and Strath Halladale. This area of sheltered to moderately exposed ground covers only 10 per cent of Sutherland but is of considerable importance to the general flora of the area, corresponding to the main limits of natural woodland. Woodland is mainly birch forest but with pine, rowan and hazel and, in some places (Assynt) oak; birch and rowan extend beyond this area into exposed sites as high as 1000 ft on Ben Loyal.

The effect of climate on vegetation is very clearly demonstrated, even to the casual observer, on the road from Bonar Bridge to Tongue. Passing along the Kyle of Sutherland the vegetation is largely wooded with some plantations. Stands of birch show a high proportion of *Betula pendula* interspersed with planted beech and oak. The decrease in tree cover becomes obvious around Lairg or on the high road above the Falls of Shin, where birch is the dominant tree and *Betula pubescens ssp odorata* the species. There is a marked change in climate to cool, rather wet, moderately exposed with moderate winters. Along Strath Tirry to Crask the climate changes mainly in having a greater exposure. Large stretches of this area, with easy access to the main road, have been planted in the past 15 years, although native trees are few and far between, occurring only in sheltered areas and away from grazing pressure. Beyond Crask there is little planting until one descends into Strath Vagastie. Here isolated trees of birch, hazel and rowan line the river side. The high area between Crask and Altnaharra is classified as cool, wet, exposed with rather severe winters. Altnaharra on the shores of Loch Naver has a much better climate. This area, described as cool, wet, moderately exposed, with moderate winters, has plantations around Altnaharra Lodge and extensive natural birch woods on the northern slopes of Ben Klibreck.

Along the shores of Loch Naver on the Bettyhill road, the climate improves rapidly so that even at Syre, some 15 miles from the coast, the climate is classified as fairly warm, rather wet, moderately exposed with moderate winters. Apart from this small area of ameliorated climate, the road to Tongue continues through an area of cool, wet, exposed country with moderate winters until one descends into the Kyle of Tongue where a remarkable change occurs over a short distance on the northern slopes of Ben Loyal.

An increasingly large area of land adjacent to this road is being planted with Sitka spruce and *Pinus contorta,* with a few amenity species on the road-side. It is the change in what is left of natural woodland which is most interesting. Two species of birch form the major tree cover with rowan, hazel and alder occurring irregularly. Although *Betula pubescens ssp. odorata* occurs wherever trees are present on this 50-mile traverse of Sutherland, *Betula pendula* is found only in three areas along the road and these coincide with the most moderate climates. At the southern end up to Inveran the species is frequent but absent from Lairg to Tongue, except for a small number at Altnaharra which may have been planted.

Botanical Districts

In his scheme for the recording of plant distribution in Great Britain, H. C. Watson divided the county of Sutherland into two vice-counties: East Sutherland (v.c. 107) the area drained by rivers flowing south-eastwards into the Moray Firth and West Sutherland (v.c. 108) where the rivers flow west and north into the Atlantic Ocean. Vice-counties are here further subdivided into smaller districts – the parishes. These parishes are based on the river systems and their mutual boundaries are, for the most part, traced along the watersheds. The parishes are as follows:

v.c. 107

CREICH   LAIRG   ROGART   DORNOCH   GOLSPIE   CLYNE   LOTH   KILDONAN

v.c. 108

ASSYNT   EDDRACHILLIS   DURNESS   TONGUE   FARR

Creich lies in the south of the county. It is bounded on the west by Assynt, on the north-west by Eddrachillis, on the north-east by Lairg and Rogart, on the east by Dornoch and on the south by Ross and Cromarty from which it is separated by the River Oykell from its source on Ben More until it flows into the Kyle of Sutherland and Dornoch Firth. The parish extends to 173 square miles and comprises the left bank basin of the Oykell river. The underlying rocks are schists of the Moine series and in the north-west Cambrian quartzite on the hill tops. The land is everywhere hilly but mountainous in the north-west where it reaches an elevation of 3273 ft on Ben More Assynt. The greater part of the parish is high bleak moorland. Arable land occurs on the low ground from Invershin to Bonar Bridge, while the lower slopes are planted with pine and oak woods. By the Kyle of Sutherland the marshy meadows are fringed with alder and willows, *Iris pseudacorus* and *Filipendula ulmaria*. The Shin valley is well wooded with birch interspersed with ash, elm, bird cherry and gean. The ground flora includes *Anemone nemorosa*, *Ajuga reptans*, *Endymion non-scriptus*, *Lysimachia nemorum*, *Oxalis acetosella*, *Trollius europaeus*, *Viola riviniana*, *Veronica chamaedrys* and the rare *Ranunculus auricomus*. In the oakwoods are found *Juniperus communis*, *Lathyrus montanus*, *Lonicera periclymenum*, *Luzula campestris*, *L. pilosa*, *L. sylvatica*, *Stellaria nemorum*, *Teucrium scorodonia* and *Trientalis europaea*. Species of *Rubus* and *Rosa* abound on the roadside. More interesting, however, is the considerable range of montane species growing at altitudes up to 3000 ft on Ben More Assynt. In addition to the commoner species such as *Alchemilla alpina*, *Arctous alpinus*, *Armeria maritima*, *Carex bigelowii*, *Cerastium alpinum*, *Empetrum*

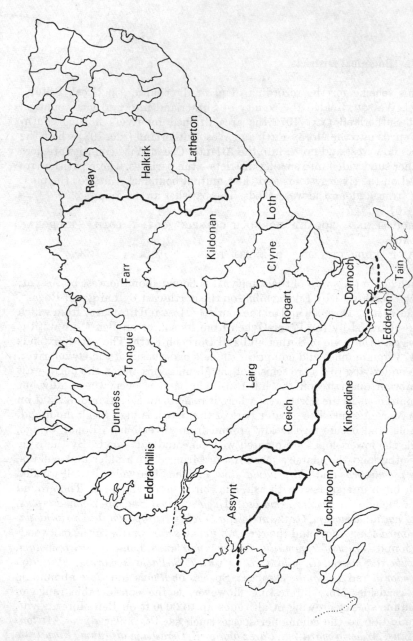

Fig. 2 County of Sutherland and adjacent counties with parish boundaries

14

hermaphroditum, Luzula spicata, Trollius europaeus, Silene acaulis there
are the rarer *Juncus trifidus, J. biglumis, J. castaneus, Draba norvegica, Poa
alpina* and *Deschampsia alpina.*

Lairg, an inland parish of 194 square miles, is bounded on the north by
Farr, on the east by Rogart, on the south by Creich and north-west by
Eddrachillis. The parish consists of the broad valley formed by the chain
of lochs – Merkland, a'Ghriama, and Shin. The hills along the watershed
north and south of the lochs rise to 1000 ft and on the northern boundary
to 2864 ft on the shoulder of Ben Hee. The numerous streamlets all drain
into the lochs. The underlying rocks are of granite and schists. The whole
area is peat covered. At Shinness, at the southern end of Loch Shin, a
considerable area has been reclaimed for agriculture. Recently the level of
the lochs has been raised by a dam at the south of Loch Shin, while a
second dam in the Shin valley below Lairg has formed a new loch
eliminating a large marsh. Extensive new forestry plantings have been
made in Strath Tirry. Accompanying these changes there has been road
reconstruction. The Flora of the parish is of a typical moorland type.

Rogart – like Lairg an inland parish – is bounded on the north by Farr,
north-east by Clyne, south-east by Golspie, south by Dornoch, south-west
by Creich and west by Lairg. Its area is 97 square miles. The northern part
of the parish is drained by the upper reaches of the Brora river and the
southern part of the Fleet river. The land is hilly with elevations ranging
from 600 to 1000 ft on the boundary hills. The rocks are of gneiss and
granite, covered with peat, so that the parish is mostly moorland and bog.
In Strath Brora and Strath Fleet there are some 2000 acres of arable land.
In the vicinity of Rogart village the following species, all very rare in the
county, are to be found: *Barbarea vulgaris, Equisetum pratense, Helianthemum chamaecistus, Lemna minor, Lepidium heterophyllum, Nuphar
pumila, Lythrum portula, Teesdalia nudicaulis* and *Vulpia myuros.*

Dornoch parish lies in the south-east of the county. It is bounded on the
west by Creich, on the north by Rogart, Golspie and Loch Fleet and on
the east and south by the Dornoch Firth. A small parish of some 34 square
miles, it has a relatively long coastline (12 miles), which is low and sandy
and fringed with dunes and links. Inland the land is hilly and rises gently
to 1100 ft in the north-west. The rocks are mainly of sandstone. The soil
near the coast is sandy, further inland of a black peaty loam bearing
coniferous plantations. The lower slopes of the hills are occupied by crofts.
Plants, very rare in Sutherland, occurring at Cuthill Sands are *Teesdalia
nudicaulis* and in a pond *Lythrum portula;* in a marsh at Dornoch *Lemna
minor, Ranunculus sceleratus* and *Typha latifolia* grow sparingly – all
threatened with extinction due to drainage. An interesting area about
1½ miles in extent lies west of Dornoch Point and shows transitions from

salt marsh to links. Characteristic plants here are *Armeria maritima*, *Aster tripolium*, *Plantago maritima*, *Salicornia europaea*, *Suaeda maritima*, *Spergularia media*, *Triglochin maritima*. Particularly on areas where turf has been removed are *Juncus gerardii*, *J. balticus*, both abundant, and *Carex maritima*, scarce. On damp grassy places grow *Coeloglossum viride*, *Listera ovata*, *Dactylorchis incarnata*, *D. purpurella* and *Centaurium littorale*. On the links *Astragalus danicus*, *Arabis hirsuta*, *Sedum acre*, *Juniperus nana*, *Empetrum nigrum*, all plentiful and *Draba incana* and *Antennaria dioica* rare. On the sandy shore *Cakile maritima*, *Salsola kali* and *Atriplex glabriuscula* abound. Another interesting area is at Cambusmore. *Saxifraga hypnoides* (at sea-level) *Helianthemum chamaecistus* both frequent, and *Agrimonia eupatoria* (scarce), while on cliff ledges *Sorbus rupicola*, *Ajuga pyramidalis* and *Orthilia secunda*, all very rare, are to be found. The birch woods here contain *Trientalis europaea*, *Melica nutans* and *M. uniflora*. In the very wet areas are *Carex remota*, *C. curta* and *Equisetum palustre*. The somewhat brackish areas at the waters edge have *Blysmus rufus* (plentiful) and *Glyceria maxima* and *Apium inundatum*, both in the only localities known in the county, scarce.

Golspie parish is bounded on the west by Rogart, on the north and north-west by Clyne, on the south-east by the Dornoch Firth and on the south by the Loch and River Fleet which separate it from Dornoch. It extends to 35 square miles. The coast is low and sandy with dunes and links but north of Golspie village it is low and rocky. On the shore at Golspie is a dense tract of *Elymus arenarius* with *Cakile maritima* and *Atriplex* species. Inland is a large triangular tract of arable land, the best in the county. On the low sandy flats and lower slopes of the hills are coniferous plantations with a ground flora of *Vaccinium myrtillus* and *Calluna*. Interesting plants here are *Goodyera repens* and *Trientalis europaea*, both species plentiful, and *Pyrola minor*, *Moneses uniflora* and *Linnaea borealis* all very scarce. The Golspie burn rises in the north and runs through the middle of the parish. In its lower course through Dunrobin Glen its banks are well wooded with alder, birch, ash, elm, oak, gean, bird cherry and goat willow. In the policies of Dunrobin Castle are many exotic trees. On the Mound rock *Saxifraga hypnoides*, *Helianthemum chamaecistus* and *Ajuga pyramidalis* – very rare. *Rosa* and *Rubus* species abound in the hedgerows and roadsides.

Clyne parish, in extent 118 square miles, is bounded on the north-west by Farr, on the north-east by Kildonan and Loth, on the south-east by the Moray Firth and on the south-west by Golspie and Rogart. The sea-coast, 3¾ miles long, is low and sandy. The underlying rocks bordering the coast are of sandstone, shale, limestone and coal; inland of schists. The land is hilly rising in the north-west to the shoulder of Ben Armine on which arise tributary streams which join the Brora river before it enters Loch

Brora. The surface is almost all moorland and rough pasture. In the birch woods bordering the loch grow *Trientalis europaea*, *Corydalis claviculata* and on rock ledges the rare *Orthilia secunda*.

Loth, the smallest parish in the county, extends to 29 square miles. It is bounded on the north by Kildonan, on the south-west by Clyne, and on the south-east by the Moray Firth. It comprises the drainage basin of the Loth river with its tributaries and several streamlets all of which reach the sea by deeply cut gorges clothed with birch and willow. The short coast line is sandy with dunes and a few rocky headlands. Inland is a narrow zone of cultivated fields with a fertile soil. In the cornfields *Centaurea cyanus* is abundant. On the roadside *Calystegia sylvatica* and *Pentaglottis sempervirens* are frequent. *Rubus* species line the hedgerows. Above the road the ground rises steeply. The lower slopes are occupied by crofts. Towards the northern boundary the hills rise to 2000 ft on Bein Uarie. The rocks are of red sandstone and on cliff ledges and screes *Sedum rosea*, *Saxifraga hypnoides*, *S. stellaris* and *Chamaepericlymenum suecicum* occur. On the moors *Alchemilla alpina*, *Lycopodium selago*, *L. alpinum* (very scarce) and *Rubus chamaemorus* grow. In Glen Sletdale *Lemna minor* has recently been recorded.

Kildonan parish comprises the drainage basin of the Helmsdale river with its tributaries and extends to 210 square miles. It is bounded on the west and north by Farr, on the east by Caithness, on the south-east by the North Sea and on the south by Loth and Clyne. The coast, scarcely 5 miles long, has a shingle beach from which the ground rises steeply while to the north of Helmsdale it is formed of cliffs rising to 650 ft at the Ord. In the north-west are many large lochs the streams from which unite to form the Helmsdale river which flows through a wide valley and passing through a narrow gap enters the sea at Helmsdale. The hills on the Caithness border range from 900 ft at the Ord to 1900 ft on Creag Scalabsdale. In the north stand the two Ben Griams each over 1900 ft, on the southern border the land rises from Eldrable hill (1338 ft) at Helmsdale to the shoulder of Ben Armine (2338 ft). The underlying rocks are granite, syenite and gneiss. The surface is for the most part, rough pasture and moorland with small areas of arable land at Kinbrace, Kildonan and Helmsdale where land has been reclaimed. In sheltered parts of the valleys scrub birch with willow are widespread. An interesting alpine flora is to be found on the upper slopes of the Ben Griams, which are topped with old red sandstone debris: *Alchemilla alpina*, *A. filicaulis*, *Arctous alpinus*, *Asplenium viride*, *Cardaminopsis petraea*, *Carex bigelowii*, *Cerastium alpinum*, *Draba incana*, *Dryas octopetala*, *Empetrum hermaphroditum Epilobium anagallidifolium*, *Galium sterneri*, *Loiseleuria procumbens*, *Luzula spicata*, *Polystichum lonchitis*, *Potentilla crantzii*, *Salix myrsinites*, *Saussurea alpina*, *Saxifraga oppositifolia* and *Sedum rosea*. In waste places round Helmsdale are some plants with restricted distribution in the county: *Bromus sterilis, Conium maculatum, Hordeum murinum, Malva sylvestris, Senecio viscosus, Torilis japonica, Veronica hederifolia* and on the railway sidings *Linaria vulgaris.*

Assynt parish lies in the south-west of the county. It is bounded on the west and north by the sea, on the east it is separated from Creich by high mountains, and on the south by rivers and lochs from Ross and Cromarty. Its area is 183 square miles. The greater part of the parish is composed of Lewisian gneiss forming bare rocky knolls with innumerable lochans in the hollows. From the gneiss rise steep Torridonian hills of red sandstone capped with Cambrian quartzite. At Inchnadamph, Elphin and Knockan are limestone plateaux flanked by cliffs. Here are to be found the most interesting plants. *Dryas octopetala* is widespread and abundant. *Asplenium viride, Agropyron donianum, Arenaria norvegica, Carex rupestris, Epipactis atrorubens, Galium sterneri, Polystichum lonchitis, Rubus saxatilis, Sorbus rupicola, Silene acaulis* and *Thalictrum alpinum* occur. On the hills *Arctous alpinus, Armeria maritima, Potentilla crantzii, Carex bigelowii, Lycopodium alpinum, L. selago, Salix myrsinites* and *Saussurea alpina* are frequent. In the lochans *Nymphaea alba, Lobelia dortmanna, Potamogeton natans, Sparganium angustifolium* and *Subularia aquatica* abound. *Trollius europaeus* is common in the fields, *Vicia orobus* on the roadsides. Notable plants on the sea-shore are *Mertensia maritima* and *Sagina saginioides*, both rare.

Eddrachillis parish, 226 square miles, is bounded on the west by the Atlantic Ocean, on the east by Durness, south-east by Lairg and Creich, and south by Assynt. The coast, much indented by fiord-like lochs, consists of precipitous cliffs interspersed by sandy and shingle bays. Inland the land is hilly, dissected by glens, and rises to 2980 ft on Foinaven and 2863 on Ben Hee. The rocks are mainly of gneiss, bare and hummocky, red sandstone hills and some limestone. Plants of the sea coast are *Silene acaulis, S. maritima, Saxifraga oppositifolia, Sedum anglicum, S. rosea, Plantago maritima, P. coronopus, Armeria maritima, Asplenium marinum, A. adiantum-nigrum, Juniperus communis ssp. nana, Populus tremula* and *Hedera helix.* In lochans are *Utricularia minor, U. intermedia, U. neglecta, Sparganium angustifolium, S. minimum, Myriophyllum alterniflorum, Nymphaea alba, Lobelia dortmanna, Subularia aquatica.* On the hills *Arctous alpinus, Acchemilla alpina, Antennaria dioica, Carex bigelowii, Empetrum hermaphroditum, Loiseleuria procumbens, Lycopodium alpinum, L. selago* are common.

Durness parish, 234 square miles, occupies the north-western corner of the county. On the north-west and north it is bounded by the Atlantic Ocean, on the east by Tongue and Farr, and on the west by Eddrachillis. It is the most sparsely populated parish in Scotland (2·4 persons per square mile). The coast is mainly of precipitous cliffs. There are two inlets, the shallow

Kyle of Durness and the longer deep-water Loch Eriboll. To the west of the Kyle is the undulating plateau – the Parphe. The rocks here are of Lewisian gneiss and Torridonian sandstone. The surface is covered with deep peat and accordingly the region is bleak moorland and peat bog. Between the Kyle and Loch Eriboll lies a range of hills attaining an elevation of nearly 3000 ft at Foinaven. The western flank of the hills is formed of gneiss and the eastern slopes of Cambrian quartzite, and so their vegetation is scanty. East of Loch Eriboll the rocks are quartzite and schists of the Moine series, resulting in a desolate moorland to the south of which stands Ben Hope (3040 ft). Forming a triangular tract round Durness village and a narrow zone on the south-western shore of Loch Eriboll are limestone rocks giving rise to good pasture land. At Balnakeil Bay there is a stretch of shell sand, which inland forms a machair.

On the cliffs at Cape Wrath and Faraid Head, *Silene acaulis* and *Saxifraga oppositifolia* are frequent. *Thalictrum alpinum* occurs on the shore at Koeldale. On the limestone *Dryas octopetala* is abundant, *Carex rupestris* and *Epipactis atrorubens* scarce. In a bog over-lying limestone near Durness these species flourish: *Pinguicula vulgaris, P. lusitanica, Drosera anglica, D. rotundifolia, Carex flacca, C. echinata, C. pulicaris, Primula scotica* and *Tofieldia pusilla.*

Common on all the hills are *Alchemilla alpina, Arctous alpinus, Arctostaphylos uva-ursi, Carex bigelowii, Empetrum nigrum, E. hermaphroditum, Juniperus communis ssp. nana, Loiseleuria procumbens, Lycopodium alpinum, L. selago, Polygonum viviparum, Salix herbacea, Saxifraga stellaris, S. oppositifolia, Saussurea alpina, Sedum rosea, Selaginella selaginoides* and *Thalictrum alpinum.* On the western cliffs of Ben Hope are *Cardaminopsis petraea, Draba norvegica, Potentilla crantzii, Salix lapponum, S. reticulata, Pyrola rotundifolia* (the only locality in the county) and *P. minor.* On the summit of Foinaven are *Armeria maritima, Cardaminopsis petraea, Cherleria sedoides, Juncus trifidus, Silene acaulis, S. maritima, Luzula spicata,* while on Meall Horn to the south *Asplenium viride, Draba incana, D. norvegica, Poa glauca, Polystichum lonchitis, Saxifraga nivalis,* are found along with other montane plants.

Tongue is bounded on the north by the Atlantic Ocean, on the east and south by Farr, and on the west by Durness. It extends to 136 square miles. The coast consists of precipitous cliffs, some sandy bays and a long shallow inlet, the Kyle of Tongue. To the west of Kyle lies the Moine, an undulating tract of bog and moor in the north of which rises Ben Hutig on which *Arctous* descends to some 500 ft. On the shores of the Kyle, Tongue woods contain many exotic trees while in the coniferous plantations grow *Listera cordata, Goodyera repens* and *Pyrola minor.* The chief river is the Borgie from Loch Loyal. *Equisetum telmateia* is found on its banks in its upper reaches, the sole locality in v.c. 108. Above Loch Loyal stands the picturesque Ben Loyal. Among the many species are *Alchemilla alpina,*

*Draba incana, Chamaepericlymenum suecicum, Epilobium anagallidifolium,
E. alsinifolium, Gnaphalium supinum, Poa glauca,* but of special interest
is the abundance of *Betula nana* in a bog between this hill and Ben Heil.
On the island off Skerray, at Melness and Coldbackie, *Radiola linoides*
occurs. At Tongue Bay *Alchemilla alpina* and *Oxyria digyna* descend to
the cliff tops.

Farr, a very large parish of 417 square miles, is bounded on the north by
the Atlantic Ocean, on the east by Caithness, on the south by Kildonan,
Clyne, Rogart and Lairg, and on the west by Eddrachiles, Durness and
Tongue. The coast consists of cliffs and sandy bays. Near the coast there
are many bare rocky outcrops. Inland the land is hilly culminating in the
south at Ben Klibreck (3154 ft) and in the south-west in Ben Hee
(2864 ft). The rocks are mainly schists of the Moine series, granite in
Strath Halladale. The parish is for the most part moorland but there is
arable land in Strathnaver, Strath Halladale and at Strathy, Kirtomy and
Bettyhill. Characteristic plants of the sea-cliffs are: *Armeria maritima,
Asplenium marinum, Cochlearia officinalis, Ligusticum scoticum, Plantago
maritima, P. coronopus, Sagina maritima, Silene maritima, Sedum rosea,
Tripleurospermum maritimum* and *Vicia sylvatica.* Plants, unusual in the
north are *Ononis repens,* a rayless form of *Senecio jacobaea* and *Tragopogon
minor* on the dunes, while in the cultivated fields *Centaurea scabiosa,
Knautia arvensis, Euphrasia brevipila* and its variety *reayensis* abound.
On the machair above Farr Bay are *Antennaria dioica, Arabis hirsuta,
Botrychium lunaria, Coeloglossum viride, Campanula rotundifolia, Draba
incana, Dryas octopetala, Listera ovata, Oxytropis halleri, Pimpinella
saxifraga, Polygonum viviparum, Primula veris* and *Salix repens.* On the
cliff tops *Primula scotica, Scilla verna* and *Euphrasia marshallii* abound.
On cliff ledges and screes from Farr to Kirtomy *Sagina saginoides* is to be
found. An area of particular interest is the hill west of the mouth of the
Naver. Here *Carex maritima* and *Dryas octopetala* are abundant. On the
cliff grow *Asplenium adiantum-nigrum, A. ruta-muraria, A. trichomanes,
Cystopteris fragilis, Epipactis atrorubens, Saxifraga aizoides* and *S. oppositifolia.* On Ben Klibreck, in addition to the common alpine species is the rare
Athyrium alpestre. In a bog nearby, the very rare sedge *Carex chordorrhiza*
has its only habitat on the mainland of Great Britain.

Botanical Exploration

Though the County of Sutherland was without roads until the beginning of the nineteenth century, several travellers had already journeyed there and recounted the hardships of travel. Pennant, who with Lightfoot, entered the county at Knockan in 1772 proceeded only a few miles further to Ledmore where he relates 'the way was impassable for horses three miles further on and that even a foot messenger must avoid the hills by crossing an arm of the sea'.

Nevertheless botanical exploration had already begun. J. Robertson (1768) (a pupil of Dr John Hope) discovered *Oxytropis halleri* at Farr in July in abundance and wrote a detailed description of the plant and its habitat accompanied with an excellent plate. He revisited the area in August to collect seed but was disappointed as only a little was to be found, the scarcity he attributed to the fact that the plants were grazed by cattle.

About this time also there existed the Hortus Siccus of Dr John Hope (Professor of Botany at Edinburgh) the species in which are listed by I. B. Balfour (1907). These included many plants from Sutherland which had been gathered over a wide area. 'At Dunrobin all along the coast is *Saxifraga tridactylites*; at Culgower, *Ajuga pyramidalis*; along the north coast, principally at Farr, *Centaurea scabiosa* (plentiful), *Gymnadenia conopsea* (frequent), *Oxytropis halleri, Primula scotica* and *Dryas octopetala*; on the north-west coast *Draba incana* and *Scutellaria galericulata* (plentiful); *Saxifraga oppositifolia* on the rocks at the sea-side at Tongue; *S. aizoides* on all the rivulets in the north; on all the high hills *Rubus chamaemorus* and *Loiseleuria procumbens* (plentiful); *Arctous alpinus* on Ben Griam and several other hills; a *Carex* (nova species) at the mouth of the Naver and *Ulmus* in Assynt.'

Thomas Pennant (1774) made a tour of Scotland in 1772 bringing with him the Rev. John Lightfoot who was to collect material for a Flora of Scotland. Lightfoot collaborated with many botanists for his *Flora Scotica* (1777). Here Dr Hope's Sutherland plants are recorded and in addition *Dryas octopetala, Asplenium viride* and *Polystichum lonchitis* which he had seen in Assynt.

W. J. Hooker (at this time Professor of Botany at Glasgow) along with W. Borrer visited many places in Scotland for material for his *Flora Scotica* (1821), in which special mention is made of some Sutherland plants. Of *Pinguicula lusitanica* he writes 'nowhere have I seen it so plentiful as in Sutherland upon the wet moors adjoining Cape Wrath. *Dryas octopetala* is common all along the coast of Sutherland; *Oxytropis halleri* at the Bay of Farr, Armadale and Invernaver; *Primula scotica* on pastures by the sea at Bighouse and Armadale Bays; *Carex maritima*, discovered at the mouth of the Naver by Dr Hope, is on the sands between the Brora and Helmsdale rivers; *Draba incana* on the heaths on the east coast at Wilkhouse Inn; *Mertensia maritima* common on the coast of Sutherland'.

On a voyage round the coast of Scotland the Rev. John Fleming (1823) – Professor of Natural History at St Andrews – called at Eriboll and noted *Chrysosplenium oppositifolium, Dryas octopetala, Phyllitis scolopendrium* and *Sedum rosea* while at Faraid Head were *Coeloglossum viride, Listera ovata, L. cordata* and *Thalictrum alpinum.*

Dr Robert Graham (1826, 1828, 1833) – Professor of Botany at Edinburgh – on three expeditions added considerably to the Flora. In 1825 on the summit of Foinaven were *Luzula arcuata, Deschampsia alpina* (*vivipara*) and *Cardaminopsis petraea* growing on disjointed quartz. More extensive explorations in 1827 and 1833 added *Luzula arcuata, Poa alpina* and *Deschampsia alpina* on Ben More Assynt. On Ben Hope, *Draba norvegica, Salix reticulata* (sparingly), *Potentilla crantzii* and *Minuartia rubella* 'of which I found a single plant somewhere on Ben Hope in 1825, but this season (1833) again in tolerable quantity on the point of one cliff.' At Koeldale he noted, '*Dryas octopetala, Thalictrum alpinum, Primula scotica* and *Glaux maritima* growing in contact forming a group which can be seen nowhere else in Britain'; *Epipactis atrorubens* in abundance at Koeldale and in Assynt on limestone rocks and in the latter place *Sorbus aria; Cladium mariscus* near Badcall in a marsh, in large quantity but flowering sparingly; *Utricularia minor,* much less common than *U. intermedia,* with one colony in flower, in Assynt; *Sarothamnus scoparius,* common in the east, occurs sparingly in the north in Strathnaver and one patch at Borgie Bridge; *Ulex europaeus,* likewise common in the east occurs all along the north coast.' These expeditions are recalled by J. H. Balfour (1865).

While the previous accounts stressed the rarer species, more comprehensive lists were recorded by H. C. Watson (1832) some ninety species noted round Golspie and (1833) about two hundred and eighty species from Farr, Tongue, Eriboll and the hills Bens Armine, Heil, Loyal and Hope. Rare and local species observed were *Fumaria capreolata* and *Draba incana* at Eriboll; *Atriplex sabulosa, Conium maculatum* and *Eupatorium cannabinum* at Farr.

In their *Guide to the Highlands and Islands of Scotland,* G. and P. Anderson (1834) list plants that are to be seen at the various localities which they describe.

Dr A. Murray (1836) of Aberdeen who had accompanied Dr Graham in 1827, produced The Northern Flora wherein are recorded all the known Sutherland plants – six being further records.

In the *New Statistical Account of Scotland* (1845) many of the Parish

Plate 3   **Carex maritima** Curved Sedge

(*J. B Kenworthy*)

Plate 4 **Chamaepericlymenum suecicum** Dwarf Cornel

accounts give some botanical information. This varies considerably according to the botanical knowledge of the compiler. There is an excellent description of the Flora of Durness by Dr Graham (1845) while in that of the parish of Tongue by H. M. McKenzie (1845) we learn of changes that are taking place. Woods have been planted with ash, beech, elm, lime, plane, larch, spruce and scots pine. Whin and broom he records as introductions. Plants such as *Lamium album* and *Silene vulgaris* probably also introduced at this time are not present now. Likewise in the parish of Loth at the Ord (since transferred to Kildonan) D. Ross notes *Primula scotica*, *Mertensia maritima* and *Vaccinium oxycoccus* none of which are present now.

While most botanists confined their attention mainly to flowering plants, W. (1857) in a wide tour of the county listed the vascular cryptogams which he observed, many being additional species. In 1883 the second edition of *Topographical Botany* was published and from this the number of species recorded can be seen (Table 1). It is interesting to note that the mountainous western areas (v.c. 108) had received more attention than the more accessible eastern region (v.c. 107). During the next 20 years all of the several botanists who visited Sutherland added many new records besides extending the distribution of known species.

James Grant of Wick collected extensively around Golspie and in Strath Halladale recording 120 new species (Bennett, 1882, 1889, 1893). Some of the more exciting ones are from the woodlands near Golspie: *Goodyera repens*, *Pyrola minor*, *Linnaea borealis* and *Orthilia secunda*. At the Mound he noted *Catabrosa aquatica* and *Apium inundatum* which were not rediscovered until recently (1962); on the sea-shore *Asplenium marinum*, *Valeriana olitoria* and *Zostera marina*, species now extinct in this area; casual species likewise extinct are *Matricaria recutita*, *Verbascum thapsus* and *Chenopodium bonus-henricus*.

W. F. Miller (1890) collected in the north of Scotland, while at Lairg some forty new species were obtained (Bennett, 1882).

Archibald Gray and L. Whinxman (1888) traversed the county in 1886 from Inverkirkaig in the west to Torrisdale in the north, described the terrain and among their collection were seventy-four species new to v.c. 108 (Bennett, 1889). A most notable discovery was *Arenaria norvegica* on the hills about Inchnadamph and on river shingle at the low elevation of 400 ft.

The Alpine Botanical Club visited Sutherland about the same time and recorded comprehensive lists (Craig, 1889) of plants from Ben Loyal, Ben Hope, Invershin, Tongue and Farr.

F. J. Hanbury made several excursions to Sutherland with H. E. Fox (1885 and 1886), with E. S. Marshall (Hanbury, 1887 and Marshall, 1891) and with J. Cosmo Melvill (Hanbury, 1889). Many critical species were recorded from Melvich, Bettyhill and Durness. Along with Marshall he first noted in Sutherland the species of *Cochlearia* later named *scotica*. A special interest of his was the genus *Hieracium* in which he named many new species several of which occur in Sutherland.

The Rev. E. S. Marshall spent a considerable time in the Highlands of Scotland over a long period (1888–1916). His many visits to Sutherland are described (1891, 1901, 1916) and along with W. A. Shoolbred (Marshall, 1897, 1898, 1909). These accounts and his extensive herbarium make a valuable contribution to the Flora of this large county. Like Hanbury he was interested in the genus *Hieracium*.

The northern forms of *Euphrasia* were another of his interests and a new species *E. marshallii* was named in his honour. With W. A. Shoolbred (Marshall, 1897) he discovered *Carex chordorrhiza* in a bog beside Loch Naver – its only locality in Britain.

G. C. Druce the author of several county floras visited Sutherland on many occasions, on three of which he wrote accounts: a visit to the limestone area at Knockan (1895), to Golspie and Invershin (1903) and in the north (1908). On these and later visits he added many additional records.

From Table 1 it will be seen that few additions were made between the appearances of the first (1905) and second (1929) supplements to Topographical Botany. During this period Crampton (1913) contributed an ecological account of the flora on Ben Armine. This contrasts with the more usual lists of species of former papers.

TABLE 1. To show number of species recorded.

		East Sutherland v.c. 107	West Sutherland v.c. 108	County of Sutherland
Topographical Botany	1883	191	307	391
1st Supplement added	1903	255	167	177
Total		446	474	568
2nd Supplement added	1925	33	34	37
Total		479	508	605
Comital Flora	1932	541	613	676
Present	1966	733	773	883

The Comital Flora (Druce, 1932) shows a great increase in the number of species recorded from the second supplement. This is in part due to variation in the concept of the species and to the recording of introduced species as well as further records.

The next account of Sutherland plants was by Wilmott and Campbell (1944) who collected in the hitherto little-worked district round Lochinver. Of the several new records, *Catapodium marinum*, *Diplotaxis muralis*, *Cephalanthera longifolia*, *Lythrum salicaria*, *Oenanthe crocata*, *Potamogeton berchtoldii* and *Sisymbrium altissimum* have their only Sutherland locations in this area.

In the more recent papers stress is laid on ecological factors. An area modified by blown sands is the plateau to the west of the estuary of the River Naver. This was explored by McVean and Berrie (1952) who recount the flora with special reference to the species of *Empetrum*.

At Inchnadamph, Raven (1952) made a notable re-discovery of the rare *Agropyron donianum* which species had previously been found by E. S. Marshall but its true identity had not been determined. The rich limestone flora of this area is more fully described by this author (1959).

There are extensive tracts of bog in Sutherland. Pearsall (1956) has described the structure of a blanket bog in the valley of the Strathy river and noted the plants typical of each area.

Foinaven – a mountain in the north-west – was visited by Blake (1959) who described the typical flora to be found in the high exposed ridges composed of Cambrian quartzite and Lewisian gneiss. This consists of *Cherleria sedoides, Armeria maritima, Silene acaulis,* all cushion plants, along with *Cardaminopsis petraea, Salix herbacea, Festuca vivipara* and *Juncus trifidus.*

The rich flora of Ben Hope was examined by Ferriera (1957, 1958, 1959) who showed that the basiphilous species are confined to a narrow band of hornblende schists on the western side of the hill. Elsewhere in the arid rocks of which the mountain is mainly composed, the flora is poor in species and similar to that found on Ben Loyal.

Of special interest are the discoveries of Ratcliffe on Meall Horn (1958), a mountain in the Reay Forest, where he observed *Saxifraga nivalis* and on Ben More Assynt (1960), a further locality for *Saxifraga nivalis* with amongst other species *Deschampsia alpina, Draba rupestris, Carex saxatilis, Juncus biglumis, J. castaneus* and *Poa alpina.* In 1962 in the south-east of the county he records *Potentilla rupestris* – a species not previously noted in Scotland.

During the past decade – as a result of the advent of the Map Scheme – the activities of many botanists have added some 200 additional species to the total recorded in the Comital Flora (Table 1).

Vegetation of Sutherland

Peculiarities of the Sutherland flora associated with individual parishes are mentioned in the relevant section of the flora (p. 13). In this section a synopsis of the general vegetation classification is included because in many cases these vegetation types are widespread and not specifically considered under each parish description. The most comprehensive vegetation classification is that of McVean and Ratcliffe (1962) in *Plant Communities of the Scottish Highlands* and this account is based largely upon the criteria they accept in their classification. The main feature of their classification system is life-form, ranging from forests through heaths to moss heaths. In most instances this agrees with a classification based upon altitudinal zonation: large trees giving way to heaths at higher altitudes and at the highest altitudes dwarf heaths or mossy heaths. This relationship, of vegetation types having specific altitudinal zones, holds for most of Scotland but in the north and north-west, i.e. Sutherland, these zones are compressed and the general altitudinal limits lowered very considerably. Thus species which normally are confined, in central Scotland, to altitudes above 2000 ft are found at sea-level in Sutherland. Species such as *Dryas octopetala*, mountain avens, *Saxifraga oppositifolia*, the purple mountain saxifrage and *Empetrum hermaphroditum*, are all found within 300 ft of sea-level at Invernaver. Such are the vagaries of climate in Sutherland that only 10 miles away on Ben Loyal the tree line reaches 1000 ft. It is apparent that the life-form of plants in any one area reflects the general environmental status and does not follow a strict altitudinal zonation for this county.

The vegetation of Sutherland can be classified under eight major headings. The most obvious of these being **forest and scrub**. Natural ashwoods are entirely absent from Sutherland although on some of the base rich soils the ground flora of hazel scrub shows a remarkable similarity with that of ash woods further south. Native pinewood with its ground flora of *Vaccinium* or *Vaccinium* plus *Calluna* is absent from Sutherland although there are pinewoods especially in the south-east of the county which show typical species associated with pinewoods. Steven and Carlisle (1959) comment on the two pinewood sites in Sutherland which might be considered as native. The first, on the islands and shores of Loch Assynt, while on areas which would not be amenable to planting, are of even age, about 100 years old and pine is not mentioned in the area in the statistical accounts. This view is confirmed by John Home's survey of Assynt (1775) in which a very detailed catalogue of all the woods in the parish of Assynt does not include pine. Secondly in the parish of Creich, on the north of Strath Oykell is a stand over 150 years in age which is considered to be a survivor of eighteenth-century plantings.

The oak and birch woodlands of Sutherland are very similar in their ground flora and it appears that birch now occupies much of the low-lying valleys previously occupied by oak. Place names may give an indication of former oakwoods: there is a Baddidarach (Gaelic, Darach – oak) both at Lochinver and near Scourie, and there is evidence of oak woodlands along the west coast and in the south east of the county. In the early eighteenth century oak bark was a valuable commodity in the area, priced at £15 per ton from woodland at Creich. Spinningdale oakwood, Creich is now scheduled as a site of scientific interest even though many of the trees appear to be approximately 130 years old (Pennie, 1966). Oak can replace birch as the dominant species up to 500 ft in the west with little or no change in the ground flora. Where oaks do survive, the associated shrub layer of holly, bird cherry and hazel is generally absent and therefore the oak woods in Sutherland do not appear as a distinct vegetation unit.

Of the woodlands to be found in Sutherland, birchwood is the most frequent ranging from the mature woodland of Drumbeg, Assynt to isolated groups of trees on the central plateau. McVean (1964) recognises two woodland types; the *Vaccinium*-rich birchwoods and the herb-rich birchwoods. The former is recognised by the presence of *Vaccinium myrtillus*, *Pteridium aquilinum* and *Deschampsia flexuosa*; the latter by the presence of *Thelypteris oreopteris* and a dominance of grass species *Anthoxanthum odoratum*, *Agrostis tenuis*. The birchwoods of the north and west have bryophytes as the main component of their ground flora. On low lying glacial drift with deep soils the herb-rich communities dominate the woodland floor, but at higher altitudes, and where boulders form the substrate, there is a luxuriant growth of many moss species. McVean (1964) lists twenty-six species from a birchwood at Loch Stack of which twelve are bryophytes. McVean and Ratcliffe (1962) referring to the same general area record the presence of sixteen tree and herb species and thirty-one bryophyte species. Many of these birchwoods appear moribund, with an even age structure and little sign of regeneration.

Other tree species particularly alder and rowan occur as single species stands though only in small areas and infrequently. Alder woodland in an open moribund state occurs at Loch Choire and McVean and Ratcliffe suggest this might be a relic of former climatic fluctuation.

Above the treeline and in places of extreme exposure sub-alpine scrub replaces woodland. In Sutherland juniper scrub is found on some islands in lochs as well as exposed situations. The juniper is normally dwarf Juniper, *Juniperus communis ssp. nana*, and is associated with lichens or bryophytes forming specialised communities at sites on Conamheall, Loch Eriboll, Foinaven and Arkle in the Reay Forest, and Farrmheall, Parphe. Mountain willow scrub is infrequent although the *Salix myrsinites* scrub of Inchnadamph is worth special note, being restricted to limestone pavement. *Salix aurita* and *S. atrocinerea* are the common species occurring in isolated patches on rock ledges and are in many cases severely wind pruned, as by the road at Coldbackie.

Dwarf shrub heath is a widespread vegetation type in the county. In a map compiled for Beekeepers by Wittles (1950), 60–70 per cent of Sutherland is shown as areas of dwarf shrub heath and the dominant species of this heath is *Calluna vulgaris*. Much of the heath is anthropogenic in origin, a living monument to man's destructive powers. Dwarf shrubs are usually characteristic of the low alpine zone, but with the retreat of the tree line in Sutherland they have spread to cover large areas.

The dry heather moor centred upon the central highlands of Scotland and dominated by *Calluna vulgaris* is not extensive in Sutherland. It is found only in the south and east of the county to any great degree and occurs in the north and west only on particularly well drained soils. At low altitudes *Erica cinerea*, *Empetrum nigrum* and *Arctostaphylos uva-ursi* are species commonly associated with *Calluna*; at high altitudes *Vaccinium spp*, *Empetrum hermaphroditum* and *Arctous alpinus* form associations. In addition at high altitudes *Calluna vulgaris* becomes dwarfed forming a dense mat of prostrate plants only a few inches in height. In central Scotland this peculiar heath form occurs at elevations above 3000 ft whereas in Sutherland it is found in the Reay Forest at the 1000 ft contour and in the extreme north of Caithness, Dunnet Head, as little as 300 ft above sea level. In general a line drawn south from Whiten Head marks the distributional limits of the lichen-rich dwarf heaths to the east and the *Rhacomitrium*-rich dwarf heaths to the west. In many areas throughout the north *Arctous alpinus* and *Calluna* form an association rich in species.

One dwarf shrub heath of particular interest in Sutherland is the *Dryas* heath. Although rare and fragmentary in Scotland, Sutherland has some of the finest *Dryas* heath in Britain. This heath is quite different to those mentioned previously in two important respects. Firstly, *Dryas* heaths are extremely rich in species; McVean and Ratcliffe (1962) report 215 different species from twenty lists made on *Dryas* heaths. Secondly, *Dryas* is found in areas where the calcium content of the soil is high. Whereas most of the *Calluna* heaths have soil pHs down to 3·5, *Dryas* heaths are alkaline and have free calcium carbonate in the soil. This situation results from the Durness limestone in the west and from calcareous shell sands along the coast of Sutherland. In Sutherland this heath occurs from sea-level at Invernaver, Bettyhill, to 1700 ft in the foothills of Ben More Assynt; further south in Scotland it reaches 3000 ft in Glen Clova. It is clear that the communities associated with *Dryas* in the north are quite different from those further south. Using data in addition to those of McVean and Ratcliffe (1962), these *Dryas* communities can be divided into three distinct types (Kenworthy, 1969); a *Dryas-Carex flacca* nodum occurs at low elevations below 300 ft, a *Dryas-Carex rupestris* nodum over a range from 200–2500 ft and a *Dryas-Salix reticulata* nodum at the highest altitudes. Although the *Dryas* communities at Invernaver are very variable and have co-dominants ranging from the dwarf shrubs *Salix repens* and *Empetrum nigrum* to bracken their association of species separates them from the other *Dryas* heaths. It would appear that this association of species dominated by *Dryas* is a unique vegetation unit dependent upon its coastal and altitudinal affinities.

Although *Calluna vulgaris* is a recurring species in the dwarf shrub heaths of Sutherland it is also a constant feature of many vegetation types which may be classified as wet heaths or **blanket bog**. Dwarf shrub heaths merge into blanket bogs wherever there is restricted drainage or a water table permanently close to the surface, and this applies to a large part of the area dominated by *Calluna*. Up to an altitude of 1500 ft *Trichophorum-Eriophorum* bog is predominant forming a typical 'hummock and hollow' type vegetation in which *Sphagnum* spp. play an important part in the process of peat accumulation. In these wetter areas *Erica tetralix* replaces *Erica cinerea*. Many insectivorous plants, such as *Drosera anglica*, *Pinguicula vulgaris*, *P. lusitanica* and *Utricularia minor* are found. Above 1500 ft *Calluna-Eriophorum* bog dominates the landscape and in many cases, north and south of Ben Loyal, by Crask Inn and at Strathy Bog, contains appreciable amounts of *Betula nana*. Also common are *Arctous alpinus* and *Rubus chamaemorus*. Where soils are shallow *Trichophorum-Calluna* bog is found, especially on ground with slopes over 10°. This vegetation type is species-poor and occurs in the western region, containing a higher proportion of lichens than previous types. There are more subtle variations upon this theme of vegetation based upon stagnant water which are not mentioned here but it is worth pointing out that these vegetation types depend almost entirely upon nutrition from rain water. Where bogs have been affected by fire drying out may take place and lead to the spread of *Rhacomitrium*. McVean and Ratcliffe (1962) point to an excellent example on the south-east end of Loch Meadie.

Soligenous mires are variants of the wetter moorland types but are grouped together on the criteria of lateral water movement through the soil, tending, in many cases, to give a richer soil and a larger number of species. They are to be found on the lower slopes of hills where lateral drainage is good. *Molinia caerulea*, *Myrica gale* and *Carex* spp. all form mire type vegetation together with *Trichophorum*, *Eriophorum* and *Calluna*. Closely associated with mires are **springs** and **flushes**, sites where there is a strong water flow, sufficient to prevent the development of closed vegetation. The moss *Cratoneuron commutatum* is a distinctive feature of flushes which are calcareous. Large patches of this rusty-golden moss often associated with *Saxifraga aizoides* can be seen from a distance against the surrounding moorland. Examples occur on the south side of Coldbackie Hill resulting from drainage water from the rich conglomerates. *Saxifraga* *aizoides* also occurs in calcareous flushes with *Carex* spp. particularly *Carex panicea* and *C. demissa* in many parts of Sutherland; Ben Stack, Glendhu, Kylesku, and on the calcareous sands at Bettyhill. In contrast acid flushes give rise to species poor vegetation dominated by *Narthecium ossifragum*, *Sphagnum* spp. and the mosses *Philonotis fontana* and *Pohlia gracilis*.

Grassland is not extensive in Sutherland except where vegetation has been intensively grazed in the south-east, the west and northern coastal fringe and along the west of the Moine Thrust. In a general sense there are three major types of which the first *Agrostis-Festuca* grassland, the most widespread, is confined to lower altitudes. This ranges from species-rich communities on soils of high base status to species-poor communities on soils of low base status. The richer types include many herbs and other grasses such as *Anthoxanthum odoratum*, while at the acidic end of the range the grass *Nardus stricta* and fewer herbs occur. At high altitudes the *Agrostis-Festuca* grassland gives way to species-poor grassland dominated by mat grass *Nardus stricta* which occurs on soils of pH 4·2–5·5. Under wetter conditions *Deschampsia caespitosa* becomes the dominant grass. Included in this section are montane grass heaths usually found at the highest altitudes, unaffected by the influence of man. In Sutherland these communities are found on the highest hills and are characteristically grass and moss mixtures, or sedges and moss. For example, a widespread type is *Nardus-Rhacomitrium* on areas with a long snow lie, generally associated with *Vaccinium myrtillus*, *Carex bigelowii* and the lichens *Cetraria islandica* and *Cladonia uncialis*. Of those montane grass heaths based upon the presence of *Juncus trifidus*, the *Juncus trifidus – Festuca ovina* type occupies much of exposed sites on mountains. The summit plateau of Ben Hope has a good example of this vegetation in which *Salix herbacea* and *Alchemilla alpina* are constants.

The two remaining units of vegetation are the **herb and fern meadow** and **moss heaths**, the latter being only slightly different from the montane grass heaths mentioned previously. Natural herb meadow is rare in Sutherland since grazing is so extensive, but it is recorded from Ben More Assynt and Meall Horn. Of a wide variety of herbs associated with this vegetation *Luzula sylvatica*, *Angelica sylvestris*, *Geum rivale* and *Sedum rosea* are constant components of the community. This vegetation is found on steep slopes where access to grazing animals is restricted. A dwarf herb meadow is to be found on Ben More Assynt dominated by *Alchemilla alpina* and *Sibbaldia procumbens* and containing *Silene acaulis*, *Thymus drucei* and *Polytrichum alpinum*.

In addition to the major vegetation types described by McVean and Ratcliffe **maritime and submaritime** communities are found along the coasts of Sutherland. These plant communities have been described in some detail by Gimingham (1964). Sutherland has a very extensive coastline including cliffs, shingle, sandy foreshores, dunes and saltmarsh. In these habitats sodium chloride from seawater or salt spray has a dominating effect upon the vegetation, except in certain dune systems where calcium carbonate from shell sand seems to be an overriding feature of the environment. Exposed cliffs harbour a large variety of lichens and dense swards of *Plantago maritima* or *Armeria maritima*. Also *Tripleurospermum maritimum* and *Ligusticum scoticum* are prominent species along the cliffs. On the cliff tops a grassland dominated by *Festuca rubra* is found sometimes associated with *Salix repens*, *Empetrum nigrum* or other prostrate shrubs where soil conditions are a little more acid. Many cliffs in northern Sutherland have both *Primula scotica* and *Scilla verna* as components of their vegetation. Where colonies of birds disturb the cliff top vegetation the area may be invaded by ruderal species. Shingle beaches are not extensive in Sutherland; *Mertensia maritima* being a most spectacular species associated with such areas. Foreshore plants seldom if ever occur in densities sufficient to produce a closed community, especially on the northern exposed beaches where communities containing *Salsola kali*, *Cakile maritima*, *Atriplex hastata* and other *Atriplex* spp. are reduced to a single representative, *Honkenya peploides* as on exposed beaches at Bettyhill.

Sand dunes are perhaps the most obvious feature of coastal vegetation. Due to their continuous state of flux they represent a range of habitats too large to be discussed here. However, the 'species richness' of a sand dune system depends to a large extent upon the chemical composition of the underlying sand. Sand derived from shell fragments has two effects. This more alkaline sand allows invasion by a wider spectrum of species and secondly the influence of such sand spreads further inland giving a greater area for colonisation. Whatever the nutrient status of the sand, Marram grass, *Ammophila arenaria*, is the dominant species in the first phases of dune formation giving rise to dune pasture and/or dune heath of some description. Due to high winds in this area most of the dune systems are in a clearly dynamic state. There are few good salt marshes in Sutherland. They are found as isolated patches at the head of the Kyles or sea lochs. Characteristic species are *Armeria maritima*, *Glaux maritima*, *Puccinellia maritima* and *Plantago maritima*: *Cochlearia officinalis* occurs sporadically but is important in many communities.

Notes on the Fungal Flora of Sutherland

by Roy Watling, Royal Botanic Gardens, Edinburgh

The fungal flora of Sutherland is poorly known, there being few published records (see Mycologia scotica, Rev. J. Stevenson, 1879) until Dennis reported on the larger fungi of the north-west Highlands of Scotland (Kew Bulletin, 1955). Dennis' paper compiles his records from Tongue and adjacent areas and with a few collections made by Henderson in the south-west corner of the county; little more was added until recently when collecting and recording has been extended along the line Cape Wrath/Duncansby Head by Watling. Sutherland is of considerable interest to the mycologist for within its boundaries one can study the fungi of northern examples of British Highland birchwood and herbaceous communities on acidic and limestone outcrops. Bettyhill is an extremely fine centre for the study of the higher fungi, particularly with its close proximity to the Strathnaver area.

The list of fungi recorded for Sutherland is in some ways little different from that of areas further south, mainly because it includes a large number of species which have been recorded by virtue of their association with the numerous plantings of 'alien' trees. It is the details of the species list and their interpretation which are of the greatest interest. However, the introduced fungal flora can indicate trends and in some cases is of particular merit. Thus Borgie forest although being a fairly mature forest is of known and comparatively recent age and therefore most if not all the members of the rich fungal flora (over 100 species can be collected within the space of a 2 hour period) have colonised since that date. The woods about Tongue House and similar established properties have even richer floras reflecting the diversity of substrata available for colonisation.

In contrast the moorlands offer very little, the dominant species being *Omphalina ericetorum*; the active *Sphagnum* areas, however, are colonised by a rather specialised and characteristic group of about a dozen species of agaric, the three most common being *Galerina paludosa*, *G. sphagnorum* and *Hypholoma elongatum*. The moorlands, where dissected by small wooded gulleys, are enriched by agarics suspected as mycorrhizal with the birches, e.g. *Russula* spp. The formerly much wider distribution of this woodland is indicated by the occurrence of agarics such as *Nolanea cetrata* and *Galerina* spp. on the slopes of Ben Loyal and neighbouring highlands. On the summits *Omphalina luteovitellina* has been recorded, a typical mountain fungus associated with the lichen *Botrydina vulgaris*.

The coastal sand-dunes offer a whole range of very characteristic species including *Conocybe dunensis* (dune brown cone-cap), *Psathyrella ammophila* (dune brittle-cap) and *Hygrophorus conicoides*. Less common species have also been collected associated with the organic crusts and *Collema* spp. found amongst the *Ammophila* plants. Undoubtedly in certain areas of the dunes as in other communities mammal dung modifies the fungal flora, i.e. colonisation by *Stropharia semiglobata*, *Panaeolus semiovatus*, etc. The coastal grasslands particularly on fixed sand are characterised by several edible species of *Agaricus* including species clearly related to both the field and horse mushrooms and by the equally edible large puff balls, e.g. *Calvatia utriformis*.

Where the latter grasslands extend to the cliff tops *Salix repens* invades the turf and although parallel communities are found in many other areas those in Sutherland are particularly rich. These communities within easy reach of Bettyhill, particularly Farr Bay, have been intensively collected over several weeks for several seasons. They are typified by *Russula* spp. (*R. persicina*, *R. fragilis*) and *Lactarius* spp. (*L. lacunarum*, *L. hysginus*) *Leccinum salicola*, *Cortinarius pseudosalor* agg., *Amanita* spp. (*A. rubescens*, undescribed species) etc. a mycorrhizal group of larger fungi and a probably saprophytic group including *Cantharellus cibarius*, a phenomenon just as one experiences in a 'normal' woodland. Grassland fungi are also intermixed in the community, e.g. *Marasmius oreades* (fairy ring champignon), *Calocybe carnea* and *Entoloma madidum*.

Undoubtedly the most interesting communities of all in Sutherland are those in the Strathnaver reserve. With its vast assemblage of flowering plants, a parallel and equally unique assemblage of higher fungi is found. *Boletus luridus* is a constant member of the *Dryas/Salix repens* nodum whereas it normally is associated elsewhere in Britain with oak woodland on base rich soils. The genera *Hebeloma* and *Inocybe* are represented by a vast assemblage of species, many of which have still to be determined because of the complexities of taxonomy; however, they are an important integral part of the flora. Even where only a few remaining plants exist the former presence of birch wood on the northern parts of the reserve is reflected by the sudden appearance in the area of woodland fungi, e.g. *Lactarius torminosus*. The *Salix repens* communities at Bettyhill are under careful observation by Watling and are being compared with similar communities at Kindrogan, Perthshire, and on Hirta in the St Kilda group. Very close parallelisms have been demonstrated and it is hoped this work will be published in the near future.

The grassland communities are frequently on acidic substrates and are fairly heavily grazed. Under these conditions the *Hygrophoraceae* play a less important part among the fruiting flora than in base-rich grasslands and are replaced by *Rhodocybe popinalis*, *Entoloma prunuloides* and *E. radiatum* and *Lycoperdon foetidum* (puff ball). In areas of high activity of sea birds the fungal flora is very depauperate resembling in constituents the area adjacent to zooplethismic grasslands on St Kilda.

The Influence of Man in Sutherland

The more one examines evidence from Sutherland the more it becomes apparent that Fraser Darling and Morton Boyd in *Natural History of the Highlands and Islands* (1964) are wrong in their assertion that 'it is possible that such areas as West Sutherland and the North West corner of Ross-shire did not know man until two or three thousand years ago'. If we accept the evidence of Callander, Cree and Ritchie (1927) that the bone caves at Allt nan Uamh had human occupants prior to the final valley glaciation it is evident that man was in this area eight to ten thousand years ago. Bones of Arctic animals were found, split for the extraction of marrow, sawn antlers of reindeer, stones burned by a fire and charcoal. No traces of domestic animals were found and it appears that man's first excursion into Sutherland was as Neolithic man, the hunter.

With an improving climate there is evidence of domesticated animals in the Neolithic chambered cairn at Embo excavated in 1960 (Henshall, 1965) where the bones of pig, sheep and small ox were found. This invasion by Mediterranean man brought with it from the 'golden crescent' of Europe cultivated crops and a more permanent culture. Several factors influenced the settlement pattern in the area. Firstly, accessibility is important and even a cursory examination shows the settlement patterns of many ages to stem largely from the coast following the sheltered straths, with their glacial soils, or to be confined to areas with an adequately amenable geology, for example, sandstones and limestones, which are easily weathered.

Little is known of these stone age peoples who buried their dead in chambered cairns. Most cairns have been pillaged in the past and little evidence of the culture remains. Neolithic peoples were gradually replaced by 'Beaker People' who buried their dead in short 'cists' or stone coffins. These coffins contained a food vessel or beaker in which have been found early cultivars. Hut circles, the remains of dwellings, seem to be the home of such people and of later bronze age settlers. That changes in the vegetation of Sutherland occurred during this period is evident from pollen analysis of deep peats and the remains of plants and animals associated with chambered cairns. Both the stumps of pine found in peat and bones of capercallie associated with cairns indicate extensive coniferous forests. Removal of the forest is evident from charcoal remains of conifers, hazel and birch together with small amounts of grain suggesting a primitive cultivation of cleared ground.

Very little is known of the bronze age peoples and their effects upon vegetation in Sutherland. It is known that these peoples who lived in an age of standing stones and circles did have at least one distinction, they cremated their dead and this at least suggests that they had some reverence for fire and that they used it extensively. Thus the process of removal of woodland may have continued in this period although there is little evidence to suggest that in Sutherland the bronze age culture was more extensive in its influence than previous cultures. It is also apparent that the tools of the early Neolithic peoples were quite effective in clearing woodland, as demonstrated in modern times in Denmark. There three men cleared 600 square yards of silver birch forest in 4 hours with an authentic axe head which had not been sharpened for four thousand years, demonstrating the potential influence of early man on forests.

Approximately 400 B.C. marks the beginning of the iron age. Lasting for some 500 years, this period includes the appearance of hill forts and the less explicit brochs. The latter, round double-walled towers up to 40 ft in height were places of refuge but there still remains much speculation about these structures. 67 brochs are listed for Sutherland but others, how many no one can guess, must have been destroyed with the passage of time. These people, the 'Caereni' of Ptolemy's map, were recognised by the Romans as a pastoral race and such observations are borne out by the presence of ox, sheep, goat and pig bones found associated with the remains of this civilisation. There is also evidence at this time of large herds of red deer. Iron used by these people required smelting and in turn required the destruction of forest, especially oak and birch. Heaps of slag indicating sites of early iron workings have been found in the immediate vicinity of two brochs at Shinness, Lairg.

Thus industry, albeit on a small scale, introduced a new factor in the destruction of forest. By this time the climate had changed to such an extent that the forests of Britain were in decline and in most parts of Sutherland removal of trees would be rapidly followed by the encroachment of moorland. Man was using a resource which would not replace itself. The scale of such impact is difficult to judge since, unlike other parts of Britain, the written history of Sutherland is particularly sparse until the seventeenth century. An inventory of ancient monuments (H.M.S.O., 1910) lists: a heap of iron slag 30 ft across and 4 ft in height near Achinduich, Lairg; heaps of slag at Kinbrace, Loch Shin; and iron slag, burnt wood plus charcoal 2½ in. thick at Skelpick, Bettyhill. Timothy Pont's map of Strath Navernia (1633) has the legend 'Heir is yron oare' on the west of Strathnaver and at the south end of Ben Stumanadh. 'Loch Isyre or ye wrights loch' refers on this map to Loch Syre. Gordon (1812) in a work written in 1630 makes reference to the inhabitants of Sutherland who 'made' iron from iron ore. Sinclair, in the first Statistical Account (1793), states of Assynt that 'Iron mines were dug here of old . . . in different places in this parish'. He also suggests that this was before the Scandinavian invasions (c. A.D. 850). The hill above Kirkton Farm, Golspie, is also referred to as the 'Iron Hill'. Thus from Assynt, to Strathnaver, to the east coast there is evidence of early iron workings and the destruction of forests.

Later wood was used in kilns in the production of limestone. In the west, particularly Assynt, there is documented evidence of tree felling for this purpose whereas further east where trees by this time were scarce peat was used in the kilns as at Strathy. Corn drying kilns are to be found in many of the pre-clearance villages and good examples are still to be found at Gruain Mor, Loch Naver and Rossal, Strathnaver. It is not clear whether peat or timber was used in those kilns but presumably where timber was available it was used. However, it can be assumed that over the past two thousand years timber of any size was becoming difficult to obtain. There is little evidence from peat profiles of pine in this period and roof timbers of 'bog oak' (pine) were highly sought after by the pre-clearance peoples in many parts of Sutherland. Apparently timbers lying in the peat could be recognised on frosty mornings by the differential frost patterns they formed.

So far emphasis has been put upon man's increasing activity in destroying woodland and the parallel deteriorating climate. But man's secondary effect is associated with his pastoral and agricultural activities. The latter were very much limited to the immediate surroundings of the village and can be seen in the excellent examples of lazy beds at Rossal and other pre-clearance villages. Grazing animals, especially sheep, goats and deer are known to suppress the regeneration of natural forest and any extension of their numbers by pastoral activities will cause a decrease in tree cover in the area. The first threat of destruction to forests was from Neolithic peoples who turned from hunting to domestication of grazing animals. There has been a general pattern of change throughout Europe which was undoubtedly followed in Sutherland. Closed forest with deer and swine gave rise to an open forest with fewer swine, and deer and cattle increase. This finally led to the virtual absence of trees and a predominance of sheep, goats and to a lesser extent, cattle.

While the grazing associated with pre-clearance villages was undoubtedly of some considerable extent it did include a variety of grazing animals, deer, cattle, 'kerry' sheep, goats and horses. Sinclair (1793) noted that in Rogart 'Some wretched vestiges of very considerable birchwoods are to be seen in different parts; but the shoots from such of the old stocks as have not decayed are annually cropped by cattle in the autumn and winter; and such shoots as may survive to a second summer are sure to be cut by the people to bind their cattle'. So the 'Caereni' or pre-clearance peoples for thousands of years would have had some adverse effects upon birch regeneration.

John Prebble in *The Highland Clearances* (1963) tells the fascinating story of the change in land management throughout Sutherland in early years of the eighteen hundreds and its disastrous sociological effects.

Whereas previously 'kerry' sheep and cattle were kept for a local market the introduction of the long faced voracious Cheviot sheep meant an export of mutton and wool to the south. Land which produced 2d. per acre under cattle now produced twelve times that amount under sheep. Over a period of 50 years the number of sheep in Sutherland built up to about 200,000 in 1857, remaining at approximately the same figure subsequently. Thus the effect of sheep over the past 100 years has been a predominant one.

That sheep farming has affected vegetation is clear from several points of view. These hardy sheep graze on the wet moorlands which cover a large part of Sutherland and in order to maintain new growth the areas are burnt. Fire reduces the possibility of natural tree regeneration. Where fire and sheep are absent as on islands in lochs (Cam Loch, Ledmore, Loch Beannach, Assynt, Loch Meadie and Loch Syre are good examples) rowan, birch and in some places oak and pine are present. This is also true of steep rock faces. In addition Pennie (1966) examined the age structure of birch woods in Strath Carnaig, which became part of the Torboll farm grazings in 1812. These birch woods are ageing, with no regeneration. The trees are no younger than 40 years and most are 80 to more than 110 years old. Grazing clearly causes a suppression of tree regeneration. He also quotes the effects of sheep fencing on the shores of Loch Choire where natural regeneration has occurred within the fenced areas.

Clearly man has influenced the vegetation of Sutherland both directly and indirectly over a period of perhaps 5000 years. Apart from the planting in the eighteenth century the present day plantings by the Forestry Commission are the first signs of man's attempts to replace some of the tree cover he has helped to remove.

Bibliography

ADAM, R. J. 1960 *John Home's Survey of Assynt* Edinburgh Scottish History Society

ANDERSON, G. & P. 1834 *Guide to the Highlands and Islands of Scotland*

ANTHONY, J. 1959 *Contribution to the Flora of Sutherland* Trans. Bot. Soc. Edinb. **38**, 7

BALFOUR, I. B. 1907 *A Catalogue of British Plants in Dr. Hope's Hortus Siccus, 1768* Notes Roy. Bot. Gard. Edinb. **4**, 147

BALFOUR, J. H. 1865 *Presidential Address* Trans. Bot. Soc. Edinb. **8**, 216

BENNETT, A. 1882 *Notes on the Flora of Caithness and Sutherland* J. Bot. Lond. **20**, 114

BENNETT, A. 1889 *Records of the Scottish Plants* Trans. Bot. Soc. Edinb. **17**, 417

BENNETT, A. 1873 *Contribution to the Flora of East Sutherland* Ann. Scot. Nat. Hist. 225

BENNETT, A. 1894 *Linnaea borealis in E. Sutherland* Ann. Scot. Nat. Hist. Soc. 249

BENNETT, A. 1894 *Contribution to the Flora of East Sutherland* Ann. Scot. Nat. Hist. 25

BENNETT, A. 1905 *Supplement to Topographical Botany* J. Bot. Lond. **43**

BENNETT, A., SALMON, C. E. & MATTHEWS, J. R. 1929–30 *Second Supplement to Topographical Botany* J. Bot. Lond. **67** and **68**

BIRSE, E. L. & DRY, F. T. 1970 *Assessment of climatic conditions in Scotland. 1. Based on Accumulated Temperature and Potential Water Deficit* Macaulay Institute, Soil Survey of Scotland

BIRSE, E. L. & DRY, F. T. 1970 *Assessment of climatic conditions in Scotland. 2. Based on Exposure and Accumulated Frost*

BLAKE, E. A. 1957 *Plant Distribution and Communities on Foinne Bheinn (Sutherland)* Trans. Bot. Soc. Edinb. **37**, 130

BOTFIELD, B. 1830 *Journal of a Tour Through the Highlands of Scotland in 1829*

BROOKS, B. S. 1964 *The Flora of Handa Island* Proc. B.S.B.I. **5**, 314

BRYCE, I. B. D. 1972 *A report on the antiquities of Bettyhill* Unpublished report

BURNETT, J. M. (ed) 1964 *The Vegetation of Scotland* Edinburgh

CALLANDER, J. G., CREE, J. E. & RITCHIE, J. 1927 *Preliminary report on caves containing palaeolithic relics near Inchnadamph, Sutherland* Proc. Soc. Antiq. Scot. **61**, 169

CAMPBELL, H. R. 1920 *Caithness and Sutherland* County Geography, Cambridge

CLAPHAM, A. R., TUTIN, T. G. & WARBURG, E. F. 1962 *Flora of the British Isles* Cambridge

CRAIG, W. 1889 *Excusion of the Scottish Alpine Botanical Club to Sutherland* Trans. Bot. Soc. Edinb. **17**, 372

CRAMPTON, C. B. & MACGREGOR, M. 1912 *Note on the Calluna-Mat Association of the Mountain Tops of the Northern Highlands (Ben Armine)* Scot. Bot. Rev. **I**, 183

CRAMPTON, C. B. & MACGREGOR, M. 1913 *The Plant Ecology of Ben Armine* Scot. Geog. Mag. **29**, 169 and 256

CRAMPTON, C. B. & MACGREGOR, M. 1913 *Note on the Calluna-Mat Association of the Mountain Tops of the Northern Highlands (Ben Armine)* Rev. J. Ecol. **I**, 219

DANDY, J. E. 1958 *List of British Vascular Plants* London

DARLING, F. F. & BOYD, J. M. 1964 *The Highlands and Islands* New Naturalist **6**, London

DONY, J. G., PERRING, F. & ROB, C. M. 1974 *English Names of Wild Flowers* Butterworths, London

DRUCE, G. C. 1895 *Notes on the Flora of Elphin* Ann. Scot. Nat. Hist. **35**

DRUCE, G. C. 1903 *Plants of East Sutherland* Ann. Scot. Nat. Hist. **37**, 122 and 286

DRUCE, G. C. 1908 *Plants of West Sutherland* Ann. Scot. Nat. Hist. **39**, 106 and 259

DRUCE, G. C. 1932 *Comital Flora of the British Isles* Arbroath

DURNO, S. E. 1958 *Pollen Analysis of Peat Deposits in Eastern Sutherland* Scot. Geog. Mag. **74**, 127

DURNO, S. E. 1958 *Occurrence of Pollen of* Fraxinus *in Northern Scottish Peats* Trans. Bot. Soc. Edinb. **37**, 220

FERRIERA, R. E. C. 1957 Salix reticulata *L. in West Sutherland* Trans. Bot. Soc. Edinb. **37**, 132

FERRIERA, R. E. C. 1958 Equisetum hyemale *L. in West Sutherland* Trans. Bot. Soc. Edinb. **37**, 220

FERRIERA, R. E. C. 1959 *Scottish Mountain Vegetation in Relation to Geology* Trans. Bot. Soc. Edinb. **37**, 229

FLEMING, J. 1823 *Gleanings of Natural History on the Coast of Scotland* Edinb. New Phil. Journ. **9**, 248

FOX, H. E. & HANBURY, P. J. 1885 *Botanical Notes of a Tour in Caithness and Sutherland* J. Bot. Lond. **23**, 333

FOX, H. E. & HANBURY, F. J. 1886 *Caithness and Sutherland Plants* J. Bot. Lond. **24**, 344

FRASER, F. S. 1870 Osmunda regalis *L. on Loch-na-Caillach, Lairg* Trans. Bot. Soc. Edinb. **10**, 460

GILMOUR, J. & WALTERS, M. 1955 *Wild Flowers* New Naturalist **5**, London

GIMINGHAM, C. H. & CORMACK, E. 1964 *Plant Distribution and Growth in Relation to Aspect on Hill Slopes in North Scotland* Trans. Bot. Soc. Edinb. **39**, 525–38

GORDON, N. J. 1963 *Invernaver National Nature Reserve, Sutherland – Management Plan* Report of Nature Conservancy

GORDON, R. 1812 *A Genealogical History of the Earldom of Sutherland from its Origin to the Year 1630* Edinburgh

GRAHAM, R. 1826 *Rare Scottish Plants* Edin. New Phil. Journ. **14**, 179

GRAHAM, R. 1827 *Botanical Excursion to Sutherland* Edin. New Phil. Journ. **4**, 193

GRAHAM, R. 1833 *Notice of Botanical Excursion into the Highlands of Scotland* Edin. New Phil. Journ. **15**, 358

GRAHAM, R. 1845 *Durness Parish Flora* New Stat. Acct. Scot. **15**, 90

GRAY, A. & HINXMAN, L. W. 1888 *A List of Plants Observed in West Sutherland* Trans. Bot. Soc. Edinb. **17**, 220

GRAY, A. 1887 Arenaria norvegica *Gunn. in Sutherland* Scot. Nat. **3**, 93

GREEN, P. S. 1955 *Pollen Grain Size in* Nasturtium Trans. Bot. Soc. Edinb. **36**, 289

HANBURY, F. J. 1886 *Botany of Caithness and Sutherland* J. Bot. Lond. **24**, 148

HANBURY, F. J. 1886 *Plants, West Sutherland and Caithness* J. Bot. Lond. **24**, 343

HANBURY, F. J. & MARSHALL, E. S. 1887 *Notes on some Plants in North Scotland* J. Bot. Lond. **25**, 125

HANBURY, F. J. & MELVILL, J. C. 1889 *Records of Sutherland Plants* J. Bot. Lond. **27**, 107

HARRISON, J. W. H. & HARRISON, H. H. 1938 *The Flora of the Island of Handa* Proc. Univ. Durham Phil. Soc. **10**, 1

HEDGE, I. 1960 *Excursion to Sutherland* Proc. B.S.B.I. **3**, 458

HENDERSON, J. 1812 *Agriculture in Sutherland* London

HENSHALL, A. S. 1965 *The Excavation of a Chambered Cairn at Embo, Sutherland* Proc. Soc. Antiq. Scot. **96**, 9

D

H.M.S.O. 1911 *Second Report and Inventory of Monuments and Constructions in the County of Sutherland* Edinburgh

HOOKER, W. J. 1821 *Flora Scotica*

HUBBARD, C. E. 1954 *Grasses* Penguin Books

INCHNADAMPH 1957 *Inchnadamph Nature Reserve* Report Nature Conservancy 47

KEEGAN, P. Q. 1889 *In Sutherland* Science Gossip **25**, 205

KEEGAN, P. Q. 1890 *The Botany of Sutherland* Science Gossip **26**, 116

KENWORTHY, J. B. 1969 Unpublished data

KENWORTHY, J. B. 1972 *The Wyllie-Fenton Field Centre, Bettyhill* Unpublished Handbook. Dept. of Botany, University of Aberdeen

KENWORTHY, J. B., ASTON, D. & BUCKNALL, S. A. 1972 *A study of hybrids between* Betula pubescens *Ehrh and* Betula nana *L. from Sutherland – an integrated approach* Trans. Bot. Soc. Edinb. **42**, 517

LIGHTFOOT, J. 1777 *Flora Scotica* London

LINTON, J. B. 1886 *New Records* (Carex pauciflora, *Ben Hope*) J. Bot. Lond. **24**, 377

LINTON, E. F. & W. R. 1889 *Records of Sutherland Plants* J. Bot. Lond. **27**, 207

LOCH, J. 1843 *Plantations on the Sutherland Estates* Trans. High. & Agr. Soc. Scot., 3rd Ser. **1**, 36

MACDONALD, J. 1880 *Agriculture in the County of Sutherland* Trans. High. Agr. Soc. Scot. **12**, 1

MACKENZIE, H. M. 1845 *Tongue Parish Flora* New Stat. Acct. Scot. **15**, 172

MCVEAN, D. N. & BERRIE, A. 1952 *Hermaphrodite* Empetrum *in Sutherland* Scot. Nat. **64**, 45

MCVEAN, D. N. 1958 *Ecology of* Alnus glutinosa (*L.*) *Gaertn* J. Ecol. **44**, 321

MCVEAN, D. N. 1958 *Island Vegetation of some West Highland Freshwater Lakes* Trans. Bot. Soc. Edinb. **37**, 200

MCVEAN, D. N. & RATCLIFFE, D. A. 1962 *Plant Communities of the Scottish Highlands* H.M.S.O. London

MCVEAN, D. N. 1964 *Dwarf Shrub Heaths*, p. 481. In, *The Vegetation of Scotland* Ed. Burnett. Edinburgh

MARSHALL, E. S. 1888 *Notes on Highland Plants* J. Bot. Lond. **26**, 149

MARSHALL, E. S. 1899 Epipactis atropurpurea (*as atrorubens*) J. Bot. Lond. **27**, 328

MARSHALL, E. S. & HANBURY, F. J. 1891 *Notes on Highland Plants* J. Bot. Lond. **29**, 108

MARSHALL, E. S. & SHOOLBRED, W. A. 1897 Carex chordorrhiza *L. f.* J. Bot. Lond. **35**, 450

MARSHALL, E. S. & SHOOLBRED, W. A. 1898 *Notes on a Tour in North Scotland* J. Bot. Lond. **36**, 166

MARSHALL, E. S. 1901 *Plants of North Scotland* J. Bot. Lond. **39**, 266

MARSHALL, E. S. & SHOOLBRED, W. A. 1909 *Some Sutherland Plants* J. Bot. Lond. **47**, 220

MARSHALL, E. S. 1910 Epipactis helleborine *var. purpurea* Celak (*as* Helleborine atroviridia) *in W. Sutherland* Ann. Scot. Nat. Hist. Soc. 123

MARSHALL, E. S. 1910 Callitriche intermedia *var. tenufolia* (*Pers.*) J. Bot. Lond. **48**, 111

MARSHALL, E. S. 1916 *Plants of West Sutherland* J. Bot. Lond. **54**, 169

MARSHALL, J. B. 1894 Betula intermedia *Thomas, in W. Sutherland* J. Bot. Lond. **23**, 78

MATTHEWS, J. R. 1955 *Origin and Distribution of the British Flora* London

MILLER, W. F. 1890 *New Records for Sutherland* J. Bot. Lond. **28**, 24

MURRAY, A. 1836 *The Northern Flora* Edinburgh

PEARSALL, W. H. 1956 *Two Blanket Bogs in Sutherland* J. Ecol. **44**, 493

PENNANT, T. 1774 *A Tour in Scotland* Chester

PENNIE, I. D. 1967 *The Influence of Man on the Vegetation of Sutherland* M.Sc. report. Dept. of Botany, University of Aberdeen

PHEMISTER, J. 1948 *Scotland, The Northern Highlands* H.M.S.O. Geological Survey Edinburgh

PERRING, F. H. & WALTERS, S. M. 1962 *Atlas of the British Flora* London and Edinburgh

PREBBLE, J. 1963 *The Highland Clearances* London

PRITCHARD, N. M. 1960 *Studies in* Gentianella amarella (*L.*) *Bor* Wats. **4**, 218

PUGSLEY, H. W. 1948 *A Prodromus of British Hieracia* J. Linn. Soc. **54**

RATCLIFFE, D. A. 1958 Saxifraga nivalis *L. in West Sutherland* Trans. Bot. Soc. Edinb. **37**, 220

RATCLIFFE, D. A. 1960 *Montane Plants in Ross-shire and Sutherland* Trans. Bot. Soc. Edinb. **39**, 107

RATCLIFFE, D. A. 1962 Potentilla rupestris *L. in Sutherland* Proc. B.S.B.I. **4**, 501

RAVEN, J. E. 1952 Agropyron doniana (*F. B. White*) *Meld* Wats. **2**, 180

RAVEN, N. E. & WALTERS, S. M. 1956 *Mountain Flowers* London

ROBERTSON, J. 1768 Oxytropis halleri *Bunge at Farr* Scot. Mag. **30**, 344

ROGERS, J. M. 1900 *Handbook of British Rubi* London

ROSS, D. 1845 *Loth Parish Flora* New Stat. Acct. Scot. **15**, 196

SALMON, C. E. 1900 *Plant Notes from Sutherland* J. Bot. Lond. **38**, 299

SALMON, C. E. 1915 Polygala oxyptera (*as dubia*) (*Dornoch*) J. Bot. Lond. **53**, 279

SIMPSON, N. D. 1960 *A Bibliographical Index of the British Flora*

SINCLAIR, J. 1763 edn *The Statistical Account of Scotland* Edinburgh

STABLES, W. 1833 Lycopodium annotinum *L. in Sutherland* Phytol. **1**, 147

STEVEN, H. M. & CARLISLE, A. 1950 *The Native Pinewoods of Scotland* Edinburgh

TIMOTHY PONT'S MAP OF STRATH NAVERNIA 1633 *Black's Atlas*

TOWNSEND, F. 1904 Galium pumilum (*as sylvestra*) *Sutherland* J. Bot. Lond. **42**, 240

TRAIL, J. W. H. 1873 Centaurea scabiosa *etc. in Sutherland* Scot. Nat. **II**, 175

W. 1857 *A Peep at the Ferns of Sutherland* Nat. **7**, 8, 29, 77

WATSON, H. C. 1832 *Plants seen at Golspie* Kew Cat. 41

WATSON, H. C. 1833 *Plants seen in North Scotland* Kew Cat. 39

WATSON, H. C. 1937 *New Botanist's Guide* **2**, 512

WATSON, H. C. 1883 *Topographical Botany* 2nd edn London

WATSON, W. C. R. 1958 *Handbook of the Rubi of Great Britain and Ireland* Cambridge

WEBSTER, M. McC & MARLER, P. 1952 *Plants of the South Parphe* Wats. **2**, 163

WHITE, I. D. & MOTTERSHEAD, D. N. 1972 *Past and Present Vegetation in Relation to Solifluction on Ben Arrkle, Sutherland* Trans. Bot. Soc. Edinb. **41**, 475–89

WILMOTT, A. J. & CAMPBELL, M. S. 1946 *Autumn Botanising at Lochinver* B.E.C. **16**, 820

WITTLES, C. L. 1950 *Heath areas in Scotland* The Scottish Beekeeper, **26**

WOLLEY-DOD, A. H. 1930–1 *A revision of the British Roses* J. Bot. Lond. **68** and **69**

YOUNG, D. P. 1959 Erinus alpinus *L. at Bettyhill* Proc. B.S.B.I. **3**, 337

Reference List of Contributors

Records have been contributed by the following

Abell, R. B.　　*R.B.A.*
Anthony, J.　　*J.A.*
Alexander, I.　　*I.A.*
Blake, E. A.　　*E.A.B.*
Brown, J.　　*J.B.*
Campbell, M. S.　　*M.S.C.*
Campbell, W. H.　　*W.H.C.*
Cardue, J. W.　　*J.W.C.*
Carrol, J.　　*J.C.*
Clarke, C. B.　　*C.B.C.*
Craig, W.　　*W.C.*
Crawford, F. C.　　*F.C.C.*
Cryer, J.　　*J.C.*
Dandy, J. E.　　*J.E.D.*
Davis, P. H.　　*P.H.D.*
Druce, G. C.　　*G.C.D.*
Duncan, U. K.　　*U.K.D.*
Exell, A. W.　　*A.W.E.*
Ferreira, R. E. C.　　*R.E.C.F.*
Flannigan, B.　　*B.F.*
Foggit, T. J.　　*T.J.F.*
Fox, H. E.　　*H.E.F.*
Goodway, K. M.　　*K.M.G.*
Gordon, G.　　*G.G.*
Graham, R.　　*R.G.*
Graham, R. A.　　*R.A.G.*
Grant, J.　　*J.G.*
Gray, A.　　*A.G.*
Hall, P. M.　　*P.M.H.*
Hanbury, F. J.　　*F.J.H.*
Harley, R. M.　　*R.M.H.*
Harrison, J. W. H-.　　*J.W.H.-H.*
Harrison, H. H-.　　*H.H.-H.*
Hedge, I.　　*I.H.*
Hood, J.　　*J.H.*
Hope, J.　　*J.H.*
Horn, G.　　*G.H.*
Johnston, G.　　*G.J.*
Kenneth, A. G.　　*A.G.K.*
Lancaster, C. R.　　*C.R.L.*
Large, K. D.　　*K.D.L.*
Ley, A.　　*A.L.*
Linton, E. F.　　*E.F.L.*
Linton, W. R.　　*W.R.L.*
Lousley, J. E.　　*J.E.L.*

McClintock, D.　　*D.McC.*
Macnab, J.　　*J.M.*
Mackechnie, R.　　*R.Mc.*
Marler, P.　　*P.M.*
Marshall, E. S.　　*E.S.M.*
Meinertzhagen, R.　　*R.M.*
Melvill, J. C.　　*J.C.M.*
Miller, W. F.　　*W.F.M.*
Milne-Redhead, H.　　*H.M.-R.*
Morrison, M.　　*M.M.*
Muirhead, C. W.　　*C.W.M.*
Oliver, D.　　*D.O.*
Palmer, R. C.　　*R.C.P.*
Proctor, M. C. F.　　*M.C.F.P.*
Pugsley, H. W.　　*H.W.P.*
Ratcliffe, D. A.　　*D.A.R.*
Raven, J. E.　　*J.E.R.*
Ribbons, B. W.　　*B.W.R.*
Riddelsdell, H. A.　　*H.A.R.*
Ross, D.　　*D.R.*
Salmon, C. E.　　*C.E.S.*
Shoolbred, W. A.　　*W.A.S.*
Sinclair, J.　　*J.S.*
Slack, A.　　*A.S.*
Sprague, T. A.　　*T.A.S.*
Stables, W. A.　　*W.A.S.*
Standen, R.　　*R.S.*
Stirling, A. McG.　　*A.McG.S.*
Summerhayes, V. S.　　*V.S.S.*
Syme, J.　　*J.S.*
Talbot, J.　　*J.T.*
Taylor, G.　　*G.T.*
Tobbit, J.　　*J.T.*
Todd, W. A.　　*W.A.T.*
Tyacken, A.　　*A.T.*
Wallace, E. C.　　*E.C.W.*
Warburg, E. F.　　*E.F.W.*
Watson, H. C.　　*H.C.W.*
Webster, M. McC.　　*M.McC.W.*
West, C.　　*C.W.*
Wickens, G. E.　　*G.E.W.*
Williamson, R. H.　　*R.H.W.*
Wilmott, A. J.　　*A.J.W.*
Young, D. P.　　*D.P.Y.*

County Flora

The sequence of genera and the nomenclature of the species are as in the List of British Vascular Plants (Dandy, 1958). The species name is followed by the vice-county number or numbers in which the species has been recorded. The common name follows that in the most recent publication on the subject *English Names of Wild Flowers* (Dony, Perring and Rob, 1974) a B.S.B.I. publication. Where an English common name is not common to Scotland the appropriate Scottish common name is given together with that recommended by the B.S.B.I. An obvious example is that of Harebell and Bluebell. All common names are to be found in *Flora of the British Isles* (Clapham, Tutin and Warburg, 1962). The next line gives the general habitat and the frequency of occurrence which is stated under:

FREQUENCY	No. of 10 km squares in which species is recorded
Very rare	1–2
Rare	3–5
Occasional	6–12
Frequent	13–40
Common	41–64
Common, widespread	65 and over

The distribution is indicated by mentioning the name of every district in which the species has been observed. The districts in the upper line are those in v.c. 107, those in the lower line of v.c. 108. As an example, when a species has been recorded from every district, its distribution is indicated thus:

CREICH	LAIRG	ROGART	DORNOCH	GOLSPIE	CLYNE	LOTH	KILDONAN
ASSYNT	EDDRACHILLIS		DURNESS	TONGUE	FARR		

When a species has not so far been recorded from a district, the name of that district is replaced by an ——, thus:

——	——	——	DORNOCH	——	——	——	KILDONAN
ASSYNT	——		——	TONGUE	——		

No further details of distribution are given except in the case of species of restricted distribution. For these the localities in which they have been

43

observed are indicated along with the date and collector's name. In such genera as *Hieracium* and *Rubus* where there are a large number of species, each with a very limited distribution, only those districts with localities where that particular species has been recorded are mentioned, thus:

Hieracium anglicum Fries (107, 108)
Dornoch (*Cambusmore*)
Assynt (*Knockan, Inchnadamph*)
Casual and introduced species of limited distribution are treated likewise.

PTERIDOPHYTA
LYCOPODIACEAE
Lycopodium L.

L. selago L. (107, 108) Fir Clubmoss
On moors, heaths and rocky places on hills. Common in the north and west. Descends to sea level on the north coast.

CREICH LAIRG ROGART DORNOCH GOLSPIE CLYNE LOTH KILDONAN
ASSYNT EDDRACHILLIS DURNESS TONGUE FARR

L. inundatum L. (108) Marsh Clubmoss
In a bog. Very rare.

—— —— —— —— ——

ASSYNT —— —— —— ——
Assynt (Canisp, 1903, G.C.D.) No recent record

L. annotinum L. (107) Interrupted Clubmoss
Stony places on hills. Very rare.

CREICH LAIRG —— —— —— —— ——

—— —— ——

Creich (Oykell Bridge, 1833, W.A.S.)
Lairg (Ben Hee, 1960, I.H.)

L. clavatum L. (107, 108) Stag's-horn or Common Clubmoss
On moors and heaths. Frequent.

—— LAIRG ROGART —— —— —— —— KILDONAN
ASSYNT —— DURNESS TONGUE ——

L. alpinum L. (107, 108) Alpine Clubmoss
On mountain moorlands. Frequent, mainly on western hills.

CREICH LAIRG ROGART —— —— —— LOTH KILDONAN
ASSYNT EDDRACHILLIS DURNESS TONGUE FARR

SELAGINELLACEAE
Selaginella Beauv.

S. selaginoides (L.) Link. (107, 108) Lesser Clubmoss
Damp mossy slopes and rock-ledges. Common.

CREICH LAIRG ROGART DORNOCH GOLSPIE CLYNE LOTH KILDONAN
ASSYNT EDDRACHILLIS DURNESS TONGUE FARR

ISOETACEAE
Isoetes L.

I. lacustris L. (107, 108) Common Quillwort

45

In lochans. Occasional.

CREICH —— —— —— —— —— — —— KILDONAN
ASSYNT —— —— —— FARR

Creich (Invershin)
Assynt (Stoer, Inchnadamph, Drumbeg)
Farr (Syre)

I. echinospora Durieu (108) Spring Quillwort
In lochans. Rare.

—— —— —— —— —— —— —— ——
ASSYNT —— —— TONGUE FARR

Assynt (Stoer, Ullapool)
Tongue (Talmine, Modsarie)
Farr (Syre)

EQUISETACEAE
Equisetum L.

E. hyemale L. (107, 108) Rough Horsetail or Dutch Rush
Wet places on hills. Very rare.

—— —— —— —— —— —— —— KILDONAN
ASSYNT —— DURNESS ——

Kildonan (Loch na Clar, 1964, A.A.S.)
Assynt (Achmore, 1886, A.G.)
Durness (Ben Hope, 1958, at 1300 ft, R.E.C.F.)

E. variegatum Schleich ex Weber & Mohr (107, 108) Variegated Horsetail
Wet banks on hills. Very rare.

CREICH —— —— —— —— —— —— ——
ASSYNT —— —— —— ——

Creich (Ben More Assynt, 1969, U.K.D.)
Assynt (Inchnadamph, 1909, E.S.M.; Lochinver, 1944, A.J.W.)

E. fluviatile L. (107, 108) Water Horsetail
In lochs, ponds and ditches. Common.

CREICH LAIRG ROGART DORNOCH GOLSPIE CLYNE LOTH KILDONAN
ASSYNT EDDRACHILLIS DURNESS TONGUE FARR

E. palustre L. (107, 108) Marsh Horsetail
In marshes and bogs. Common.

CREICH LAIRG ROGART DORNOCH GOLSPIE CLYNE LOTH KILDONAN
ASSYNT EDDRACHILLIS DURNESS TONGUE FARR

E. sylvaticum L. (107, 108) Wood Horsetail

46

Wet woodlands, banks and sandy places. Frequent.

CREICH LAIRG ROGART DORNOCH GOLSPIE CLYNE LOTH KILDONAN
ASSYNT EDDRACHILLIS DURNESS TONGUE FARR

E. pratense Ehrh. (107, 108) Shady Horsetail
On grassy banks. Rare.

—— LAIRG ROGART —— —— CLYNE —— ——
ASSYNT —— DURNESS —— ——

Lairg (Lairg, 1857, W.)
Rogart (Tressady, 1957, M.McC.W.)
Clyne (Brora, 1957, M.McC.W.)
Assynt (Drumbeg)
Durness (Ben Hope, 1970, R.W.M.C.)

E. arvense L. (107, 108) Field Horsetail
Waste places, fields, roadsides and dunes. Common.

CREICH LAIRG ROGART DORNOCH GOLSPIE CLYNE LOTH KILDONAN
ASSYNT EDDRACHILLIS DURNESS TONGUE FARR

E. × litorale Kühlew ex Rupr. (107)
Clyne (Brora, M.McC.W., 1957)

E. telmateia Ehrh. (107, 108) Great Horsetail
Muddy banks of streams. Rare.

—— —— ROGART —— —— CLYNE —— ——
—— —— —— —— TONGUE ——

Rogart (Tressady, 1957, M.McC.W.)
Clyne (Brora, 1957, M.McC.W.)
Tongue (Borgie, 1959, B. & T.)

OSMUNDACEAE
Osmunda L.

O. regalis L. (107, 108) Royal Fern
Boggy places in the north and west. Occasional.

—— LAIRG —— —— —— —— —— ——
ASSYNT EDDRACHILLIS DURNESS TONGUE ——
Lairg (Loch na-Caillach, 1870, F.S.F.)

HYMENOPHYLLACEAE
Hymenophyllum Sm.

H. wilsonii Hook. (107, 108) Wilson's Filmy-fern
Wet rocks and woods in the west. Occasional.

CREICH —— —— —— —— —— —— ——
ASSYNT EDDRACHILLIS DURNESS TONGUE FARR

DENNSTAEDTIACEAE
Pteridium Scop.

P. aquilinum (L.) Kühn (107, 108) Bracken
Woods, banks, heaths and moors. Common, widespread.
CREICH LAIRG ROGART DORNOCH GOLSPIE CLYNE LOTH KILDONAN
ASSYNT EDDRACHILLIS DURNESS TONGUE FARR

ADIANTACEAE
Cryptogramma R. Br.

C. crispa (L.) R. Br. ex Hook (108) Parsley Fern
Rocky places. Very rare.

――― ――― ――― ――― ――― ――― FARR
Farr (Ben Klibreck, 1956, E.F.W.)

BLECHNACEAE
Blechnum L.

B. spicant (L.) Roth (107, 108) Hard-fern
Woods, banks and rocky places on moors. Common, widespread.
CREICH LAIRG ROGART DORNOCH GOLSPIE CLYNE LOTH KILDONAN
ASSYNT EDDRACHILLIS DURNESS TONGUE FARR

ASPLENIACEAE
Phyllitis Hill

P. scolopendrium (L.) Newm. (107, 108) Hart's-tongue
Shady rock crevices. Occasional in the north and west, very rare in
the east.
――― ――― ――― DORNOCH ――― ――― ――― ―――
ASSYNT EDDRACHILLIS DURNESS TONGUE FARR
Dornoch (Cambusmore, 1962, A.McG.S.)

Asplenium L.

A. adiantum-nigrum L. (107, 108) Black Spleenwort
Rocky places, banks and walls. Frequent.
――― LAIRG ――― GOLSPIE CLYNE LOTH KILDONAN
ASSYNT EDDRACHILLIS DURNESS TONGUE FARR

A. marinum L. (107, 108) Sea Spleenwort
Sea-cliffs and caves on north and west coasts. Occasional. Extinct in east.

48

—— —— —— —— GOLSPIE —— —— ——
ASSYNT EDDRACHILLIS DURNESS TONGUE FARR
Golspie (Strathsteven, 1888, J.G., 1897, E.S.M.)

A. trichomanes L. (107, 108) Maidenhair Spleenwort
Rock-crevices and walls. Frequent in the west, scarce in the east.
CREICH LAIRG ROGART DORNOCH GOLSPIE CLYNE LOTH KILDONAN
ASSYNT EDDRACHILLIS DURNESS TONGUE FARR

A. viride Huds. (107, 108) Green Spleenwort
On wet basic rocks. Occasional.
CREICH —— —— —— —— —— ——
ASSYNT EDDRACHILLIS DURNESS TONGUE FARR

A. ruta-muraria L. (107, 108) Wall-rue
Walls and basic rocks. Occasional in the north and west, rare in east.
—— —— —— DORNOCH GOLSPIE —— —— ——
ASSYNT EDDRACHILLIS DURNESS TONGUE FARR

ATHYRIACEAE
Athyrium Roth

A. filix-femina (L.) Roth (107, 108) Lady Fern
Shady woods and banks. Common.
CREICH LAIRG ROGART DORNOCH GOLSPIE CLYNE LOTH KILDONAN
ASSYNT EDDRACHILLIS DURNESS TONGUE FARR

A. alpestre (Hoppe) Rylands (107, 108) Alpine Lady Fern
Mountain screes. Rare.
CREICH —— —— —— —— —— ——
—— —— —— —— FARR
Creich (Ben More Assynt, 1891, E.S.M. & F.J.H.)
Farr (Ben Klibreck, 1887, E.S.M.)

Cystopteris Bernh.

C. fragilis (L.) Bernh. (107, 108) Brittle Bladder-fern
Basic rocks and walls. Frequent.
CREICH —— —— DORNOCH GOLSPIE —— LOTH KILDONAN
ASSYNT EDDRACHILLIS DURNESS TONGUE FARR

ASPIDIACEAE
Dryopteris Adans.

D. filix-mas (L.) Schott (107, 108) Male Fern

49

Woods and shady places. Common, widespread.

CREICH LAIRG ROGART DORNOCH GOLSPIE CLYNE LOTH KILDONAN
ASSYNT EDDRACHILLIS DURNESS TONGUE FARR

D. borreri Newm. (107, 108) Scaly or Golden-scaled Male Fern
Damp shady places in woods and amongst rocks. Frequent.

CREICH LAIRG ROGART DORNOCH GOLSPIE CLYNE LOTH KILDONAN
ASSYNT EDDRACHILLIS DURNESS TONGUE FARR

D. abbreviata (DC) Newm. (107, 108) Small Male Fern
Rocky places on hills. Rare.

CREICH —— —— —— —— —— —— ——
ASSYNT EDDRACHILLIS —— —— FARR

D. lanceolatocristata (Hoffm.) Alston (108) Narrow Buckler-fern
Moist woodlands. Occasional.

—— —— —— —— —— —— —— ——
ASSYNT EDDRACHILLIS DURNESS TONGUE FARR

D. dilatata (Hoffm.) A. Gray (107, 108) Broad Buckler-fern
Shady places in woods and heaths. Common, widespread.

CREICH LAIRG ROGART DORNOCH GOLSPIE CLYNE LOTH KILDONAN
ASSYNT EDDRACHILLIS DURNESS TONGUE FARR

D. aemula (Ait.) Kuntze (108) Hay-scented Buckler-fern
On rocks in Birchwoods. Very rare.

—— —— —— —— —— —— —— ——
—— EDDRACHILLIS DURNESS —— ——
Eddrachillis (*Loch Stack, 1963, D.A.R.*)
Durness (*Loch Eriboll, 1965, D.McC.*)

D. assimilis S. Walker (107, 108)
On cliffs. Very rare.

CREICH —— —— —— —— —— —— ——
ASSYNT EDDRACHILLIS DURNESS ——
Creich (*Ben More Assynt, 1890, F.J.H., 1891, E.S.M.*)
Assynt (*Achmelvich, 1955, J.A.*)
Eddrachillis (*Ben Stack, 1967, A.G.K.*)
Durness (*Ben Hope, 1966, A.G.K.: Foinaven, 1967, A.G.K.: Carnstackie,
1967, A.G.K.: Loch Eriboll, 1967, D.McC.*)

Polystichum Roth

P. aculeatum (L.) Roth (107, 108) Hard Shield-fern
Shady places amongst rocks and in woods. Occasional.

——————	——————	——————	DORNOCH	——————		——————	——————	KILDONAN
ASSYNT	EDDRACHILLIS		DURNESS	——————		FARR		

P. lonchitis (L.) Roth (107, 108) Holly Fern
Crevices in basic rocks. Occasional on limestone rocks.

CREICH	——————	——————		——————	——————		——————	——————	KILDONAN
ASSYNT	——————		DURNESS	——————		FARR			

THELYPTERIDACEAE
Thelypteris Schmidel

T. oreopteris (Ehrh.) Slosson (107, 108) Lemon-scented or Mountain Fern
Moist places on heaths, banks and mountains. Common, widespread.

CREICH	LAIRG	ROGART	DORNOCH	GOLSPIE	CLYNE	LOTH	KILDONAN
ASSYNT	EDDRACHILLIS	DURNESS	TONGUE	FARR			

T. phegopteris (L.) Slosson (107, 108) Beech Fern
Moist rocks and in woods. Frequent in north and west, rare in east.

CREICH	——————	ROGART	DORNOCH	——————		——————	——————	KILDONAN
ASSYNT	EDDRACHILLIS	DURNESS	TONGUE	FARR				

T. dryopteris (L.) Slosson (107, 108) Oak Fern
Screes and rocks on hills and woods. Occasional.

CREICH	——————	——————	DORNOCH	——————		CLYNE	LOTH	KILDONAN
ASSYNT	EDDRACHILLIS	DURNESS	TONGUE	FARR				

T. robertiana (Hoffm.) Slosson (108) Limestone Fern
Limestone screes. Rare.

ASSYNT	——————		——————	——————	——————	——————

Assynt (Inchnadamph)

POLYPODIACEAE
Polypodium L.

P. vulgare L. (107, 108) Polypody
Woods, banks and walls. Common, widespread.
sub sp. **vulgare**

CREICH	LAIRG	ROGART	DORNOCH	GOLSPIE	CLYNE	LOTH	KILDONAN
ASSYNT	EDDRACHILLIS	DURNESS	TONGUE	FARR			

sub sp. **prionodes** Rothm.

CREICH	——————	——————		——————	——————		——————	——————	KILDONAN
——————	EDDRACHILLIS	DURNESS	TONGUE	FARR					

MARSILEACEAE
Pilularia L.

P. globulifera L. (107) Pillwort
Creich (Invershin, 1834, R.G., Plentiful, 1840, W.H.C., Shin Bridge, 1893, A.B.)
Now extinct.

OPHIOGLOSSACEAE
Botrychium Sw.

B. lunaria (L.) Sw. (107, 108) Moonwort
Pastures, dunes and moors. Frequent.

| —— | —— | —— | DORNOCH | GOLSPIE | —— | —— | KILDONAN |
| ASSYNT | EDDRACHILLIS | | DURNESS | TONGUE | FARR | | |

Ophioglossum L.

O. vulgatum L. (108) Adder's-tongue
Grassy places. Rare.

| —— | —— | —— | —— | —— | —— | —— | —— |
| ASSYNT | EDDRACHILLIS | | DURNESS | —— | —— | | |

SPERMATOPHYTA
GYMNOSPERMAE
PINACEAE
Pinus L.

P. sylvestris L. (107, 108) Scots Pine
Widely planted throughout the county.

| CREICH | LAIRG | ROGART | DORNOCH | GOLSPIE | CLYNE | LOTH | KILDONAN |
| ASSYNT | EDDRACHILLIS | | DURNESS | TONGUE | FARR | | |

CUPRESSACEAE
Juniperus L.

J. communis L. (107, 108) Juniper
On heaths, dunes, moors, sea-cliffs, mountain rocks and woods.
Common. Very variable from gnarled prostrate plants to shrubs
4 ft high.
Includes
sub sp. **communis**, sub sp. **nana** and intermediate forms.

| CREICH | LAIRG | ROGART | DORNOCH | GOLSPIE | CLYNE | LOTH | KILDONAN |
| ASSYNT | EDDRACHILLIS | | DURNESS | TONGUE | FARR | | |

ANGIOSPERMAE
DICOTYLEDONES
RANUNCULACEAE
Caltha L.

C. palustris L. (107, 108) Marsh Marigold
Marshes, ditches and banks of streams. Ascends to 2500 ft on Ben More.
Common, widespread.

CREICH LAIRG ROGART DORNOCH GOLSPIE CLYNE LOTH KILDONAN
ASSYNT EDDRACHILLIS DURNESS TONGUE FARR

sub sp. **palustris**. The Commoner form.

sub sp. **minor** (Mill.) Clapham. Frequent in the north and on hills.

Trollius L.

T. europaeus L. (107, 108) Globe-flower
In damp pastures, fields and mountains. Common at sea-level in the
north and west.

CREICH LAIRG ROGART ——— ——— CLYNE ——— KILDONAN
ASSYNT EDDRACHILLIS DURNESS TONGUE FARR

Anemone L.

A. nemorosa L. (107, 108) Wood Anemone
Woodlands. Frequent in the south-east, local elsewhere.

CREICH LAIRG ROGART DORNOCH GOLSPIE CLYNE LOTH KILDONAN
ASSYNT EDDRACHILLIS ——— TONGUE FARR

Ranunculus L.

R. acris L. (107, 108) Meadow Buttercup
Meadows, fields and roadsides. Common, widespread. Ascends to 2500 ft.

CREICH LAIRG ROGART DORNOCH GOLSPIE CLYNE LOTH KILDONAN
ASSYNT EDDRACHILLIS ——— TONGUE FARR

R. repens L. (107, 108) Creeping Buttercup
Fields and waste places. Common, widespread.

CREICH LAIRG ROGART DORNOCH GOLSPIE CLYNE LOTH KILDONAN
ASSYNT EDDRACHILLIS DURNESS TONGUE FARR

R. bulbosus L. (107, 108) Bulbous Buttercup
Dry grassland and dunes. Occasional in sandy coastal areas in the
east and north.

CREICH LAIRG ROGART DORNOCH GOLSPIE CLYNE LOTH KILDONAN
ASSYNT EDDRACHILLIS DURNESS TONGUE FARR

R. auricomus L. (107) Goldilocks Buttercup
Woodlands. Very rare.
CREICH ―― ―― ―― CLYNE ―― ――
―― ―― ―― ―― ―― ――

Creich (Shin Falls, 1960, J.A.)
Clyne (Loch Brora, 1957, M.McC.W.)

R. flammula L. (107, 108) Lesser Spearwort
Marshes, ditches and lochans. Common, widespread.
CREICH LAIRG ROGART DORNOCH GOLSPIE CLYNE LOTH KILDONAN
ASSYNT EDDRACHILLIS DURNESS TONGUE FARR

R. sceleratus L. (107) Celery-leaved Buttercup
Muddy bank of stream. Very rare.
―― ―― ―― DORNOCH ―― ―― ―― ――
―― ―― ―― ―― ―― ――

Dornoch (Dornoch, 1955, J.A.)

R. hederaceus L. (107, 108) Ivy-leaved Crowfoot
Muddy banks of ditches, ponds. Frequent.
―― ―― ROGART DORNOCH GOLSPIE CLYNE LOTH KILDONAN
ASSYNT EDDRACHILLIS ―― ―― FARR

R. trichophyllus Chaix (108) Thread-leaved Water-crowfoot
sub sp. **drouetii** (Godr) Clapham
Lochans. Rare.
―― ―― ―― ―― ―― ――
ASSYNT DURNESS TONGUE FARR

R. aquatilis L. (108) Common Water-crowfoot
Lochans. Rare.
―― ―― ―― ―― ―― ――
DURNESS ―― FARR

Durness (Durness)
Farr (Melvich)

R. ficaria L. (107, 108) Lesser Celandine
sub sp. **ficaria**
Woods and shady banks. Frequent.
CREICH LAIRG ROGART DORNOCH GOLSPIE CLYNE LOTH KILDONAN
ASSYNT EDDRACHILLIS DURNESS TONGUE FARR

54

(*J. B. Kenworthy*)

Plate 5 **Rubus chamaemorus** Cloudberry

Thalictrum L.

T. alpinum L. (107, 108) Alpine Meadow-rue
Rocky slopes on hills. Frequent on western hills. At sea-level on north
coast.
CREICH LAIRG ROGART —— —— —— —— KILDONAN
ASSYNT EDDRACHILLIS DURNESS TONGUE FARR

T. minus L. (107, 108) Lesser Meadow-rue
On coastal dunes and limestone rocks. Frequent.
—— —— —— DORNOCH GOLSPIE CLYNE LOTH KILDONAN
ASSYNT EDDRACHILLIS DURNESS TONGUE FARR

sub sp. **montanum** Wallr. On limestone rocks.
Durness (*Durness, 1897, E.S.M., 1950, J.A.*)
Tongue (*Melness, 1900, E.S.M.*)

sub sp. **arenarium** (Butcher) Clapham. On coastal dunes.

BERBERIDACEAE
Berberis L.

B. vulgaris L. (108) Barberry
Woods. Introduced.
Tongue (*Tongue*).

NYMPHAEACEAE
Nymphaea L.

N. alba L. (107, 108) White Water-lily
In lochs and lochans. Frequent in the north and west, local in east.
CREICH LAIRG ROGART —— GOLSPIE CLYNE —— KILDONAN
ASSYNT EDDRACHILLIS DURNESS TONGUE FARR

Nuphar Sm.

N. pumila (Timm) DC. (107) Least Water-lily
In a lochan. Very rare.
Rogart (*Little Rogart, 1960, M.McC.W. Only locality*)

PAPAVERACEAE
Papaver L.

P. rhoeas L. (108) Common or Field Poppy
On railway track. Casual. Very rare.
Farr (*Forsinard*)

E

P. dubium L. (107, 108) Long-headed Poppy
Roadsides and fields. Occasional in the east, rare in north.

			DORNOCH	GOLSPIE	CLYNE	LOTH	KILDONAN
ASSYNT	EDDRACHILLIS		DURNESS	TONGUE	FARR		

P. somniferum L. (107) Opium Poppy
Garden Escape.

CREICH	—	—	—	—	—	—	KILDONAN
—	—		—	—	—		

Creich (Bonar Bridge)
Kildonan (Kildonan)

Meconopsis Vig.

M. cambrica (L.) Vig. (107, 108) Welsh Poppy
Introduced.

CREICH	—	—	—	—	—	—	—
ASSYNT	—		—	—	—		

Creich (Invershin)
Assynt (Inchnadamph)

Chelidonium L.

C. majus L. (107) Greater Celandine
Introduced.
Kildonan (Kildonan)

FUMARIACEAE
Corydalis Medic.

C. claviculata (L.) DC. (107, 108) Climbing Corydalis or White
Climbing Fumitory
Amongst rocks in woods and scrub. Occasional.

				GOLSPIE	CLYNE	—	KILDONAN
ASSYNT	—		DURNESS	TONGUE	FARR		

Golspie (Morvich)
Clyne (Gordonbush, Strath Brora)
Kildonan (Helmsdale)
Assynt (Elphin, Beannach)
Tongue (Rhi-Tongue)
Farr (Grumore)

Fumaria L.

F. capreolata L. (108) White Ramping Fumitory

56

Fields. Very rare.

—— —— —— —— —— —— —— ——
—— EDDRACHILLIS DURNESS —— ——
Eddrachillis (Kinlochbervie)
Durness (Eriboll)

F. bastardii Bor. (107, 108) Tall Ramping Fumitory
In cultivated fields. Very rare.

—— —— —— —— GOLSPIE —— —— ——
ASSYNT —— —— ——
Golspie (Golspie)
Assynt (Achmelvich)

F. muralis Sond. ex Koch (108) Common Ramping Fumitory
sub sp. **boraei** (Jord.) Pugsl. Fields. Rare

—— —— —— —— TONGUE FARR —— ——
Tongue (Tongue)
Farr (Bettyhill)

F. officinalis L. (107, 108) Common Fumitory
Fields and waste places. Frequent.

CREICH LAIRG ROGART DORNOCH GOLSPIE CLYNE LOTH KILDONAN
ASSYNT EDDRACHILLIS DURNESS TONGUE FARR

CRUCIFERAE
Brassica L.

B. napus L. (107, 108) Rape
Fields. Introduced. Frequent in east, rare in west.

CREICH LAIRG ROGART DORNOCH GOLSPIE CLYNE LOTH KILDONAN
ASSYNT —— —— —— FARR

B. rapa L. (108) Wild Turnip
Fields. Introduced.
Assynt (Lochinver)

Sinapis L.

S. arvensis L. (107, 108) Charlock
Fields. Frequent.

CREICH LAIRG ROGART DORNOCH GOLSPIE CLYNE LOTH KILDONAN
ASSYNT EDDRACHILLIS DURNESS TONGUE FARR

S. alba L. (107, 108) White Mustard

Fields. Introduced. Rare.

| CREICH | —— | —— | —— | GOLSPIE | —— | —— | —— |
| —— | —— | —— | —— | TONGUE | FARR | | |

Creich (*Invershin*)
Golspie (*Golspie*)
Tongue (*Tongue*)
Farr (*Bettyhill*)

Diplotaxis DC.

D. muralis (L.) DC. (108) Annual Wall-rocket
Casual. Very rare.
Assynt (*Lochinver*)

Raphanus L.

R. raphanistrum L. var. **aureum** Wilmott (107, 108) Wild Radish
Cultivated fields. Frequent.

| CREICH | LAIRG | ROGART | DORNOCH | GOLSPIE | CLYNE | LOTH | KILDONAN |
| ASSYNT | EDDRACHILLIS | | DURNESS | TONGUE | FARR | | |

Crambe L.

C. maritima L. (107) Sea Kale
On foreshore at Dunrobin Gardens. Recorded in 1903 by G. C. Druce
with the note that it may be a domestic cabbage which was established
on the beach.

Cakile Mill.

C. maritima Scop. (107, 108) Sea Rocket
On sandy seashore. Occasional.

| —— | —— | —— | DORNOCH | GOLSPIE | CLYNE | LOTH | KILDONAN |
| ASSYNT | EDDRACHILLIS | | DURNESS | TONGUE | FARR | | |

Lepidium L.

L. heterophyllum Benth (*L. smithii Hook*) (107) Smith's Pepperwort or
Smith's Cress
Roadsides and fields. Rare.

| —— | LAIRG | ROGART | —— | —— | —— | —— | KILDONAN |
| —— | —— | | —— | —— | —— | | |

L. latifolium L. (107) Dittander
Introduced. Recorded 1833 by H. C. Watson without locality.

58

Thlaspi L.

T. arvense L. (107) Field Penny-cress
Roadsides, waste places and fields on east coast. Rare.

—— —— —— DORNOCH GOLSPIE CLYNE LOTH KILDONAN
—— —— ——

Teesdalia R. Br.

T. nudicaulis (L.) R. Br. Shepherd's Cress
In sandy places. Very rare.

—— —— ROGART DORNOCH —— —— ——
—— —— ——

Rogart (Tressady, 1951, M.McC.W.)
Dornoch (Cuthill Sands, 1960, J.A.)

Capsella Medic.

C. bursa-pastoris (L.) Medic. (107, 108) Shepherd's-purse
Waste places, roadsides and fields. Frequent.

CREICH LAIRG ROGART DORNOCH GOLSPIE CLYNE LOTH KILDONAN
ASSYNT EDDRACHILLIS DURNESS TONGUE FARR

Cochlearia L.

C. officinalis L. (107, 108) Common Scurvy-grass
Sea-cliffs, shingle shores and salt-marshes. Frequent.

CREICH —— —— DORNOCH GOLSPIE CLYNE LOTH KILDONAN
ASSYNT EDDRACHILLIS DURNESS TONGUE FARR

C. alpina (Bab.) H. C. Wats. (107, 108) Alpine Scurvy-grass
Rock-ledges on mountains, rare.

CREICH —— —— —— —— —— ——
DURNESS TONGUE ——

Creich (Ben More Assynt)
Durness (Ben Hope)
Tongue (Ben Loyal)

C. scotica Druce (108) Scottish Scurvy-grass
Coastal rocks and shingle. Rare. On north and west coasts.

—— —— —— —— —— —— ——

ASSYNT EDDRACHILLIS DURNESS TONGUE FARR

C. danica L. (108) Danish Scurvy-grass
On sandy sea-shores. Rare.

Tongue (Kyle of Tongue)
Farr (Invernaver)

Subularia L.

S. aquatica L. (107, 108) Awlwort
Sandy margins of lochans. Occasional. Rare in the east.

			DORNOCH				
ASSYNT	EDDRACHILLIS	DURNESS					

Dornoch (Loch Buidhe)

Lunaria L.

L. annua L. (107) Honesty
Garden escape.
Clyne (Brora, 1949, W.A.T.)

Draba L.

D. norvegica Gunn. (107, 108) Rock Whitlow-grass
Rock-ledges on mountains. Very rare.

CREICH							
		DURNESS					

Creich (Ben More, 1888, A.G.: 1959, D.A.R.)
Durness (Ben Hope, 1833, J.M.; Meall Horn, 1959, D.A.R.)

D. incana L. (107, 108) Hoary Whitlow-grass
Sandy turf by the sea and rock-ledges on mountains. Frequent.

CREICH		DORNOCH	GOLSPIE			KILDONAN
ASSYNT		DURNESS	TONGUE	FARR		

Erophila DC.

E. verna (L.) Chevall. (107, 108) Common or Spring Whitlow-grass
On dry banks, grassland and walls. Frequent in east, rare and near sea
in north and west.

CREICH		DORNOCH	GOLSPIE	CLYNE		KILDONAN
ASSYNT	EDDRACHILLIS	DURNESS	TONGUE	FARR		

Cardamine L.

C. pratensis L. (107, 108) Cuckooflower or Lady's Smock
In damp pastures. Common, widespread.

CREICH LAIRG ROGART DORNOCH GOLSPIE CLYNE LOTH KILDONAN
ASSYNT EDDRACHILLIS DURNESS TONGUE FARR

C. flexuosa With. (107, 108) Wavy Bitter-cress or Wood Bitter-cress
In moist shady places. Common.
CREICH LAIRG ROGART DORNOCH GOLSPIE CLYNE LOTH KILDONAN
ASSYNT EDDRACHILLIS DURNESS TONGUE FARR

C. hirsuta L. (107, 108) Hairy Bitter-cress
Waste places, roadsides, walls. Common.
CREICH LAIRG ROGART DORNOCH GOLSPIE CLYNE LOTH KILDONAN
ASSYNT EDDRACHILLIS DURNESS TONGUE FARR

Barbarea R. Br.

B. vulgaris (L.) R. Br. (107, 108) Winter-cress or Yellow Rocket
Moist banks. Very rare.
—— —— ROGART —— —— —— —— ——
—— —— —— —— —— FARR
Rogart (Rogart, 1959, M.McC.W.)
Farr (Altnaharra, 1885, F.J.H.)

Cardaminopsis (C. A. Mey) Hayek

C. petraea (L.) Hiit. (107, 108) Northern Rock-cress
Cliffs and quartz screes on hills. Rare.
—— —— —— —— —— —— —— KILDONAN
—— —— —— DURNESS —— ——
Kildonan (Ben Griam Beg, 1962, A.McC.S.)
Durness (Foinaven, summit, 1833, J.M., 1957, E.A.B.)

var. **hispida** DC.
Durness (Ben Hope, 1833, J.M., 1900; E.S.M., 1914, G.C.D.; 1959, J.A.)

Arabis L.

A. hirsuta (L.) Scop. (107, 108) Hairy Rock-cress
On dunes, banks and basic rocks. Occasional.
—— —— —— DORNOCH GOLSPIE —— —— ——
ASSYNT EDDRACHILLIS DURNESS TONGUE FARR

Rorippa Scop.

R. nasturtium-aquaticum (L.) Hayek (107, 108) Water-cress
In streams and ditches. Occasional.

61

CREICH   LAIRG   ———   DORNOCH ——— CLYNE ———
———   ———   DURNESS TONGUE FARR

R. microphylla (Boenn.) Hyland (107, 108) One-rowed Water-cress
In ditches. Occasional.
———   ———   ———   DORNOCH GOLSPIE CLYNE LOTH   KILDONAN
———   ———   DURNESS TONGUE FARR

Hesperis L.

H. matronalis L. (107, 108) Dame's Violet
Shady damp places. Garden escape. Occasional.
CREICH LAIRG ———   DORNOCH GOLSPIE CLYNE LOTH   KILDONAN
ASSYNT ———

Alliaria Scop.

A. petiolata (Bieb.) Cavara et Grande (107) Garlic Mustard or
Jack-by-the-Hedge
Roadsides. Rare.
CREICH ———   ———   DORNOCH ———   ———   ———   KILDONAN
———   ———   ———   ———   ———

Sisymbrium L.

S. officinale (L.) Scop. (107, 108) Hedge Mustard
Waste places. Occasional.
CREICH ———   ———   DORNOCH GOLSPIE ———   LOTH   KILDONAN
ASSYNT ———   ———   ———   FARR

S. altissimum L. (108) Tall Rocket
Waste places. Casual. Very rare.
Assynt (*Lochinver, 1944, A.J.W.*)

Arabidopsis (DC.) Heynh.

A. thaliana (L.) Heynh. (107, 108) Thale Cress
Roadsides, waste places. Frequent in the east, very rare in west.
CREICH LAIRG ROGART DORNOCH GOLSPIE CLYNE LOTH   KILDONAN
ASSYNT ———   ———   ———   FARR

Descurainia Webb & Berth

D. sophia (L.) Webb ex Prantl. (107) Flixweed
Waste places. Very rare.

62

Dornoch (Dornoch, 1952, J.A.; Poles, 1960, J.A.)
Golspie (Golspie, 1898, E.S.M. & W.A.S.)

RESEDACEAE
Reseda L.

R. luteola L. (107) Weld or Dyer's Rocket
On the railway bank. Casual.
Creich (Invershin, 1888, W.C.)

VIOLACEAE
Viola L.

V. riviniana Reichb. (107, 108) Common Dog-violet
On banks, heaths and woods. Common, widespread.
CREICH LAIRG ROGART DORNOCH GOLSPIE CLYNE LOTH KILDONAN
ASSYNT EDDRACHILLIS DURNESS TONGUE FARR

V. canina L. (107, 108) Heath Dog-violet
On dunes, heaths and dry banks. Frequent in coastal areas in the north
and west.
—— LAIRG —— —— —— —— —— ——
ASSYNT EDDRACHILLIS DURNESS TONGUE FARR

V. lutea Huds. (108) Mountain Pansy
On mountain grassland. Very rare.

ASSYNT —— —— TONGUE ——
Assynt (Inchnadamph, 1886, A.G.)
Tongue (Ben Loyal, 1888, W.C.)

V. tricolor L. (107, 108) Wild Pansy
sub sp. **tricolor**. Cultivated ground and waste places. Frequent.
sub sp. **curtisii** (Forst.) Syme. On dunes.
CREICH LAIRG ROGART DORNOCH GOLSPIE CLYNE LOTH KILDONAN
ASSYNT EDDRACHILLIS DURNESS TONGUE FARR

V. arvensis Murr. (107, 108) Field Pansy
Cultivated fields. Occasional in east, rare in north and west.
CREICH LAIRG ROGART DORNOCH GOLSPIE CLYNE LOTH KILDONAN
ASSYNT —— —— TONGUE FARR

POLYGALACEAE
Polygala L.

P. vulgaris L. (107, 108) Common Milkwort
Dry, basic grassland and rocks. Common.
CREICH LAIRG ROGART DORNOCH GOLSPIE CLYNE LOTH KILDONAN
ASSYNT EDDRACHILLIS DURNESS TONGUE FARR

P. serpyllifolia Hose (107, 108) Heath Milkwort
Heaths and pastures. Common, widespread.
CREICH LAIRG ROGART DORNOCH GOLSPIE CLYNE LOTH KILDONAN
ASSYNT EDDRACHILLIS DURNESS TONGUE FARR

GUTTIFERAE
Hypericum L.

H. androsaemum L. (108) Tutsan
Introduced. Very rare.
Assynt (Lochinver, 1944, A.J.W.)

H. perforatum L. (107) Perforate or Common St John's-wort
On banks. Very rare.
Kildonan (Kinbrace, 1882, J.G.)

H. maculatum Crantz (107) Imperforate St John's-wort
sub sp. **obtusiusculum** (Tourlet) Hayek
On banks. Introduced.
Lairg (Lairg)

H. tetrapterum Fr. (107) Square-stalked St John's-wort
Moist banks. Rare.
—— —— ROGART —— —— —— —— KILDONAN
—— —— —— —— —— ——

H. pulchrum L. (107, 108) Slender St John's Wort
Grassy places and heaths. Common, widespread.
CREICH LAIRG ROGART DORNOCH GOLSPIE CLYNE LOTH KILDONAN
ASSYNT EDDRACHILLIS DURNESS TONGUE FARR

CISTACEAE
Helianthemum Mill.

H. chamaecistus Mill. (107) Common Rockrose
On banks and rocks. Rare.

CARYOPHYLLACEAE
Silene L.

S. vulgaris (Moench) Garcke (107, 108) Bladder Campion
Cultivated ground. Rare.
— — — — GOLSPIE — LOTH —
— — — — — FARR

S. maritima With. (107, 108) Sea Campion
Shingle shores and cliffs. Frequent on north and west coast; local in east.
— — — DORNOCH GOLSPIE — — KILDONAN
ASSYNT EDDRACHILLIS DURNESS TONGUE FARR

S. acaulis (L.) Jacq. (107, 108) Moss Campion
Rock-ledges and cliffs on hills, on sea-cliffs, on west and north coasts.
Frequent.
CREICH — — — — — KILDONAN
ASSYNT EDDRACHILLIS DURNESS TONGUE FARR

S. dioica (L.) Clairv. (107, 108) Red Campion
Sea-cliffs, banks and woodland. Common.
CREICH LAIRG ROGART DORNOCH GOLSPIE CLYNE LOTH KILDONAN
ASSYNT EDDRACHILLIS DURNESS TONGUE FARR

S. alba (Mill.) E. H. L. Krause (107, 108) White Campion
Fields, roadsides. Occasional.
— LAIRG — DORNOCH GOLSPIE — — KILDONAN
ASSYNT — DURNESS TONGUE FARR

Lychnis L.

L. flos-cuculi L. (107, 108) Ragged Robin
Marshes, common.
CREICH LAIRG ROGART DORNOCH GOLSPIE — LOTH KILDONAN
ASSYNT EDDRACHILLIS DURNESS TONGUE FARR

Cerastium L.

C. arvense L. (107, 108) Field Mouse-ear
Sandy places. Occasional.
— — ROGART — — — — KILDONAN
— — DURNESS TONGUE FARR

C. tomentosum L. (107) Snow-in-summer
Garden escape.
Kildonan (*Kildonan*)

C. alpinum L. (107, 108) Alpine Mouse-ear
Screes and ledges on mountains. Rare.

CREICH —— —— —— —— —— —— KILDONAN
—— —— DURNESS TONGUE ——

Creich (*Ben More, Rosehall*)
Kildonan (*Ben Griam Mor and Beg*)
Durness (*Foinhaven, Ben Hope*)
Tongue (*Ben Loyal*)

C. arcticum Lange (107) Arctic Mouse-ear
Rocks on mountains. Very rare.

CREICH —— —— —— —— —— —— ——
—— —— —— —— —— ——

Creich (*Conival, 1908, E.S.M. & F.J.H., 1959, D.A.R.*)

C. holosteoides Fr. Common Mouse-ear
C. fontanum Baumg.
sub sp. **trivale** (Murb.) Jalas (107, 108)
Grassy places and waste ground. Common, widespread.

CREICH LAIRG ROGART DORNOCH GOLSPIE CLYNE LOTH KILDONAN
ASSYNT EDDRACHILLIS DURNESS TONGUE FARR

sub sp. **scoticum** Jalas & P. D. Sell (108)
Farr (*Strathy*)

C. glomeratum Thuill. (107, 108) Sticky Mouse-ear
Roadsides and cultivated land. Common.

CREICH LAIRG ROGART DORNOCH GOLSPIE CLYNE LOTH KILDONAN
ASSYNT EDDRACHILLIS DURNESS TONGUE FARR

C. atrovirens Bab. (107, 108) Sea Mouse-ear or Dark-green Mouse-ear
Sandy places near the sea. Occasional.

—— —— —— DORNOCH GOLSPIE CLYNE LOTH KILDONAN
ASSYNT EDDRACHILLIS DURNESS TONGUE FARR

C. semidecandrum L. (107, 108) Little Mouse-ear
Dry sandy places near the sea. Rare.

CREICH —— —— —— GOLSPIE —— —— ——
ASSYNT —— DURNESS TONGUE ——

Stellaria L.

S. media (L.) Vill. (107, 108) Common Chickweed
Cultivated ground and waste places. Common, widespread.
CREICH   LAIRG   ROGART   DORNOCH   GOLSPIE   CLYNE   LOTH   KILDONAN
ASSYNT   EDDRACHILLIS   DURNESS   TONGUE   FARR

S. pallida (Dumort.) Piré (107) Lesser Chickweed
Sandy ground by the sea. Rare.
———   ———   ———   ———   GOLSPIE   ———   ———   ———
———   ———   ———   ———   ———   ———

Golspie (Loch Fleet, 1897, E.S.M., 1960, J.A.)

S. neglecta Weihe (108) Greater Chickweed
Shady places. Rare.
ASSYNT   ———   ———   ———   ———   FARR   ———   ———   ———
Assynt (Inchnadamph, 1890, E.S.M.)
Farr (Bettyhill, 1889, F.J.H., 1960, J.A.)

S. holostea L. (107, 108) Greater Stitchwort
Woodlands and scrub. Common.
CREICH   LAIRG   ROGART   DORNOCH   GOLSPIE   CLYNE   LOTH   KILDONAN
ASSYNT   ———   DURNESS   TONGUE   FARR

S. graminea L. (107, 108) Lesser Stitchwort
Grassy heaths and woodlands. Common.
CREICH   LAIRG   ROGART   DORNOCH   GOLSPIE   CLYNE   LOTH   KILDONAN
ASSYNT   ———   DURNESS   TONGUE   FARR

S. alsine Grimm (107, 108) Bog Stitchwort
Ditches, marshes, woodlands. Common.
CREICH   LAIRG   ROGART   DORNOCH   GOLSPIE   CLYNE   LOTH   KILDONAN
ASSYNT   EDDRACHILLIS   DURNESS   TONGUE   FARR

Sagina L.

S. apetala Ard. (107, 108) Annual Pearlwort
Bare places. Rare.
———   ———   ———   ———   ———   CLYNE   ———   ———
———   ———   ———   ———   TONGUE   ———
Clyne (Balnacoil, 1957, M.McC.W.)
Tongue (Tongue, 1957, M.McC.W.)

S. ciliata Fr. (107) Fringed Pearlwort

Bare ground. Very occasional.

	LAIRG		DORNOCH		CLYNE		KILDONAN

S. maritima Don (107, 108) Sea Pearlwort
Sea-cliffs and salt marshes. Very occasional.

			DORNOCH	GOLSPIE			KILDONAN
ASSYNT			DURNESS	TONGUE	FARR		

S. procumbens L. (107, 108) Procumbent Pearlwort
Waste places. Common, widespread.

CREICH	LAIRG	ROGART	DORNOCH	GOLSPIE	CLYNE	LOTH	KILDONAN
ASSYNT	EDDRACHILLIS		DURNESS	TONGUE	FARR		

S. saginoides (L.) Karst. (107, 108) Alpine Pearlwort
Cliff-ledges on mountains, sea-cliffs, bare gravelly places. From sea-level
to 2900 ft. Rare.
Creich (Ben More, 1960, D.A.R.)
Assynt (Stoer, 1959, J.A.)
Eddrachillis (Eylestrome, 1964, J.A.)
Tongue (Ben Loyal, 1888, W.C.)
Farr (Farr Bay, Swordly, Kirtomy, Strathnaver, Skelpick, 1960, J.A.)

S. subulata (Sw.) Presl. (107, 108) Heath or Awl-leaved Pearlwort
Dry sandy and gravelly places. At 2000 ft at Ben Hope. Frequent in the
north and west.

		ROGART					KILDONAN
ASSYNT	EDDRACHILLIS		DURNESS	TONGUE	FARR		

S. nodosa (L.) Fenzl (107, 108) Knotted Pearlwort
On wet sand and dunes by the sea. Occasional.

			DORNOCH	GOLSPIE		LOTH	
ASSYNT	EDDRACHILLIS		DURNESS	TONGUE	FARR		

Minuartia L.

M. rubella (Wahlenb.) Hiern (108) Mountain or Alpine Sandwort
Mountain cliffs. Very rare. Not seen for many years.
Durness (Ben Hope, 1833, R.G.)

Cherleria L.

C. sedoides L. (107, 108) Cyphel
On mountain screes to 2900 ft. Frequent on mountains in the north and
west. On Ben Griam in the east.

68

CREICH ———— ———— ———— ———— ———— ———— KILDONAN
ASSYNT EDDRACHILLIS DURNESS TONGUE FARR

Honkenya Ehrh.

H. peploides (L.) Ehrh. (107, 108) Sea Sandwort
On coastal sand and shingle. Frequent.
———— ———— ———— DORNOCH GOLSPIE CLYNE LOTH KILDONAN
ASSYNT EDDRACHILLIS DURNESS TONGUE FARR

Moehringia L.

M. trinervia (L.) Clairv. (107) Three-nerved Sandwort
In woodlands. Rare.
———— ———— ROGART DORNOCH ———— ———— ———— ————
———— ———— ———— ————

Rogart (Rogart)
Dornoch (Cambusmore)

Arenaria L.

A. serpyllifolia L. (107, 108) Thyme-leaved Sandwort
On bare ground, dunes and fields. Occasional.
sub sp. **serpyllifolia**
CREICH LAIRG ROGART DORNOCH GOLSPIE CLYNE LOTH KILDONAN
ASSYNT EDDRACHILLIS DURNESS TONGUE FARR

sub sp. **leptoclados** (Reichb.) Nyman. Slender Sandwort
———— ———— ———— ———— ———— ———— ————
———— ———— DURNESS TONGUE ————

A. norvegica Gunn. sub sp. **norvegica** (108) Arctic or Norwegian
Sandwort
Rocks on hills and river shingle. Very rare.
———— ———— ———— ———— ———— ————
ASSYNT ————
Assynt (Inchnadamph)

Spergula L.

S. arvensis L. (107, 108) Corn Spurrey
Cultivated fields. Common.
CREICH LAIRG ROGART DORNOCH GOLSPIE CLYNE LOTH KILDONAN
ASSYNT EDDRACHILLIS DURNESS TONGUE FARR

Spergularia (Pers) J. & C. Presl

S. rubra (L.) J. & C. Presl (107, 108) Sand Spurrey
Bare sandy and gravelly places. Occasional.

| —— | LAIRG | ROGART | DORNOCH | GOLSPIE | —— | —— | KILDONAN |
| —— | EDDRACHILLIS | | DURNESS | TONGUE | FARR | | |

S. media (L.) C. Presl (107, 108) Greater Sea-spurrey
Muddy places in salt-marshes. Very occasional.

| —— | —— | —— | DORNOCH | GOLSPIE | —— | —— | —— |
| ASSYNT | —— | | —— | TONGUE | FARR | | |

S. marina (L.) Griseb. (107, 108) Lesser Sea-spurrey
In salt-marshes. Rare.

| —— | —— | —— | DORNOCH | GOLSPIE | —— | —— | —— |
| ASSYNT | —— | | —— | TONGUE | FARR | | |

ILLECEBRACEAE
Scleranthus L.

S. annuus L. (107) Annual Knawel
Sandy waste ground. Old record.
Golspie (*Golspie, 1888, J.G.*)

PORTULACACEAE
Montia L.

M. fontana L. sub sp. **lamprosperma** Cham. (107, 108) Blinks
In wet places, springs, ditches. Common, widespread.

| CREICH | LAIRG | ROGART | DORNOCH | GOLSPIE | CLYNE | LOTH | KILDONAN |
| ASSYNT | EDDRACHILLIS | | DURNESS | TONGUE | FARR | | |

M. perfoliata (Willd.) Howell (107) Spring Beauty or Perfoliate Purslane
Cultivated ground. Rare.

| —— | —— | —— | DORNOCH | GOLSPIE | CLYNE | —— | —— |
| —— | —— | —— | —— | —— | —— | | |

M. sibirica (L.) Howell (107, 108) Pink Purslane
By streams and on damp ground. Introduced. Occasional.

| —— | LAIRG | —— | —— | GOLSPIE | CLYNE | LOTH | KILDONAN |
| ASSYNT | —— | | —— | —— | FARR | | |

CHENOPODIACEAE
Chenopodium L.

C. bonus-henricus L. (107) Good King Henry
Golspie (*Golspie Tower, 1888, J.G.*) *Old Record.*

70

C. album L. (107, 108) Fat Hen
In cultivated ground and waste places. Frequent.
CREICH LAIRG ROGART DORNOCH GOLSPIE CLYNE LOTH KILDONAN
ASSYNT EDDRACHILLIS DURNESS TONGUE FARR

C. rubrum L. (108) Red Goosefoot
Assynt (Lochinver, 1886, A.G.) Old Record.

    Atriplex L.

A. littoralis L. (107) Grass-leaved Orache or Shore Orache
Sea-shore. Rare.
—— —— —— DORNOCH —— —— —— ——

Dornoch (Ferrytown, 1960, J.A.)

A. patula L. (107, 108) Common Orache
Cultivated fields and waste places. Occasional.
—— LAIRG —— DORNOCH GOLSPIE —— —— KILDONAN
ASSYNT EDDRACHILLIS DURNESS TONGUE FARR

A. hastata L. (107, 108) Hastate Orache or Spear-leaved Orache.
Waste places. Occasional.
—— —— —— —— GOLSPIE —— —— KILDONAN
ASSYNT —— DURNESS TONGUE FARR

A. glabriuscula Edmondst. (107, 108) Babington's Orache
On sandy and shingly shores. Occasional on all coasts.
—— —— —— DORNOCH GOLSPIE CLYNE LOTH KILDONAN
ASSYNT EDDRACHILLIS DURNESS TONGUE FARR

A. laciniata L. (107) Frosted Orache
On sandy sea-shores. Rare
—— —— —— DORNOCH GOLSPIE —— —— ——
—— —— —— FARR
Farr (Farr, Bettyhill, 1833, H.C.W.)

    Suaeda Forsk. ex Scop.

S. maritima (L.) Dumort. (107) Annual Seablite
On salt-marshes. Rare.
—— —— —— DORNOCH GOLSPIE —— —— ——

Dornoch (Ferrytown, Dornoch, Skelbo)
Golspie (Loch Fleet)

71

Salsola L.

S. kali L. (107, 108) Prickly Saltwort
On sandy shores. Rare.

——— ——— ——— DORNOCH GOLSPIE ——— ——— ———
——— EDDRACHILLIS ——— TONGUE FARR
Dornoch (Dornoch)
Golspie (Golspie)
Eddrachillis (Loch Laxford, Sandwood)
Tongue (Melness)
Farr (Melvich)

Salicornia L.

S. europaea L. (107, 108) Glasswort
Muddy salt-marshes. Rare.

——— ——— ——— DORNOCH GOLSPIE ——— ——— ———
——— ——— ——— ——— TONGUE ———
Dornoch (Ferrytown, Dornoch, Skelbo, Cambusmore)
Golspie (Loch Fleet)
Tongue (Kyle of Tongue)

TILIACEAE
Tilia L.

T. × europaea L. (107, 108) Common Lime
Introduced. Widely planted in the south-east, sparse in north-west.
CREICH LAIRG ROGART DORNOCH GOLSPIE CLYNE LOTH KILDONAN
ASSYNT EDDRACHILLIS ——— TONGUE FARR

MALVACEAE
Malva L.

M. moschata L. (107, 108) Musk Mallow
Grassy banks. Garden escape. Occasional.

——— ——— ROGART DORNOCH GOLSPIE ——— ——— KILDONAN
——— ——— ——— ——— TONGUE ———

M. sylvestris L. (107) Common Mallow
Waste places. Occasional.

——— ——— ——— DORNOCH GOLSPIE CLYNE ——— KILDONAN
——— ——— ———

M. neglecta Wallr. (107) Dwarf Mallow
Waste places. Rare.

72

— — — — GOLSPIE — — KILDONAN
— — — — — —

Golspie (Golspie)
Kildonan (Helmsdale)

LINACEAE
Linum L.

L. catharticum L. (107, 108) Fairy Flax or Purging Flax
Heaths, moors, pastures, dunes. Common, widespread.
CREICH LAIRG ROGART DORNOCH GOLSPIE CLYNE LOTH KILDONAN
ASSYNT EDDRACHILLIS DURNESS TONGUE FARR

Radiola Hill

R. linoides Roth (107, 108) All-seed
On bare sandy soil. Rare and local.
— — — — GOLSPIE — — —
— — — — TONGUE —
Golspie (Golspie, 1957, M.McC.W.)
Tongue (Eilean Iosal, 1886, A.G., Eilean nan Ron, 1929, J.T.,
Achininver & Coldbackie, 1960, J.A.)

GERANIACEAE
Geranium L.

G. pratense L. (107) Meadow Cranesbill
Introduced. Rare.
— — — — GOLSPIE — — KILDONAN
— — — — — —

G. endressii Gay (107) French Cranesbill
On roadsides. Introduced.
CREICH — — DORNOCH — — — KILDONAN
— — — — — —

G. dissectum L. (107, 108) Cut-leaved Cranesbill
Grassy and waste places. Occasional.
CREICH LAIRG ROGART DORNOCH GOLSPIE — — KILDONAN
ASSYNT EDDRACHILLIS — — FARR

G. molle L. (107, 108) Dove's-foot Cranesbill
Dunes, fields, roadsides, waste places. Common, widespread.
CREICH LAIRG ROGART DORNOCH GOLSPIE CLYNE LOTH KILDONAN
ASSYNT EDDRACHILLIS DURNESS TONGUE FARR

73

G. pusillum L. (107, 108) Small-flowered Cranesbill
In grassland. Rare.

| —— | —— | ROGART | —— | GOLSPIE | —— | —— | —— |
| —— | —— | | —— | TONGUE | —— | | |

Rogart (*Rogart, 1957, M.McC.W.*)
Golspie (*Golspie, 1957, M.McC.W.*)
Tongue (*Rabbit Island, 1962, C.R.L.*)

G. robertianum L. (107, 108) Herb Robert
Shady banks, walls and shingle shores. Common.

| CREICH | LAIRG | ROGART | DORNOCH | GOLSPIE | CLYNE | LOTH | KILDONAN |
| ASSYNT | EDDRACHILLIS | | DURNESS | TONGUE | FARR | | |

Erodium L'Hérit.

E. cicutarium (L.) L'Hérit. (107, 108) Common Storksbill
sub sp. **dunense** Andreas
Grassy and sandy places. Occasional.

| —— | —— | —— | DORNOCH | —— | CLYNE | LOTH | KILDONAN |
| ASSYNT | —— | | —— | TONGUE | FARR | | |

OXALIDACEAE
Oxalis L.

O. acetosella L. (107, 108) Wood-sorrel
In woods and shady places amongst rocks on hills. Common, widespread.

| CREICH | LAIRG | ROGART | DORNOCH | GOLSPIE | CLYNE | LOTH | KILDONAN |
| ASSYNT | EDDRACHILLIS | | DURNESS | TONGUE | FARR | | |

BALSAMINACEAE
Impatiens L.

I. glandulifera Royle (107) Indian Balsam or Policeman's Helmet
Introduced. Waste places.
Golspie (*Golspie*)

ACERACEAE
Acer L.

A. pseudoplatanus L. (107, 108) Sycamore
Introduced, widely planted throughout the county.

HIPPOCASTANACEAE
Aesculus L.

A. hippocastanum L. (107) Horse-chestnut
Commonly planted in eastern areas.

AQUIFOLIACEAE
Ilex L.

I. aquifolium L. (107, 108) Holly
Amongst rocks on hills. Occasional in north and west. Introduced in
south and east.

CREICH ——— ROGART DORNOCH ——— ——— ——— ———
ASSYNT EDDRACHILLIS DURNESS TONGUE FARR

LEGUMINOSAE
Ulex L.

U. europaeus L. (107, 108) Gorse
Roadsides, old woodlands, heaths. Common, widespread.

CREICH LAIRG ROGART DORNOCH GOLSPIE CLYNE LOTH KILDONAN
ASSYNT EDDRACHILLIS DURNESS TONGUE FARR

U. gallii Planch. (107, 108) Western Gorse or Dwarf Furze
On heaths. Very rare.

——— ——— ——— ——— ——— ——— ——— KILDONAN
ASSYNT ——— ——— ——— ———
Kildonan (Kinbrace, 1962, M.McC.W.)
Assynt (Lochinver, 1944, A.J.W. & M.S.C.)

Sarothamnus Wimm.

S. scoparius (L.) Wimmer ex Koch (107, 108) Broom
Amongst scrub and on heaths. Common in the east, sparse (introduced)
in north and west.

CREICH LAIRG ROGART DORNOCH GOLSPIE CLYNE LOTH KILDONAN
ASSYNT ——— DURNESS TONGUE FARR

Ononis L.

O. repens L. (107, 108) Common Restharrow
On dunes. Rare.

——— ——— ——— ——— GOLSPIE ——— ——— ———
——— ——— ——— ——— FARR
Golspie (Golspie)
Farr (Bettyhill, Farr)

Medicago L.

M. sativa L. (108) Lucerne
In cultivated fields. Casual.
Farr (Farr Bay, 1957, J.A.)

M. lupulina L. (107, 108) Black Medick
Fields, dunes and waste places. Occasional.

| —— | —— | —— | DORNOCH | GOLSPIE | CLYNE | —— | KILDONAN |
| —— | EDDRACHILLIS | | DURNESS | —— | FARR | | |

Melilotus Mill.

M. alba Medic. White Melilot
In cultivated field. Casual.
Farr (Farr Bay, 1958, J.A.)

Trifolium L.

T. pratense L. (107, 108) Red Clover
Fields and pastures. Common.

| CREICH | LAIRG | ROGART | DORNOCH | GOLSPIE | CLYNE | LOTH | KILDONAN |
| ASSYNT | EDDRACHILLIS | | DURNESS | TONGUE | FARR | | |

T. medium L. (107, 108) Zigzag Clover
Pastures. Occasional.

| —— | —— | —— | GOLSPIE | —— | —— | KILDONAN |
| —— | EDDRACHILLIS | —— | —— | FARR | | |

T. hybridum L. (107, 108) Alsike Clover
Fields and roadsides. Occasional.

| —— | —— | —— | DORNOCH | —— | —— | —— | KILDONAN |
| —— | EDDRACHILLIS | DURNESS | TONGUE | FARR | | | |

T. repens L. (107, 108) White Clover
Pastures, dunes and roadsides. Common, widespread.

| CREICH | LAIRG | ROGART | DORNOCH | GOLSPIE | CLYNE | LOTH | KILDONAN |
| ASSYNT | EDDRACHILLIS | | DURNESS | TONGUE | FARR | | |

T. campestre Schreb. (107, 108) Hop Trefoil
Grassy places in dunes. Occasional.

| —— | —— | —— | DORNOCH | GOLSPIE | CLYNE | LOTH | KILDONAN |
| —— | —— | | DURNESS | TONGUE | FARR | | |

T. dubium Sibth. (107, 108) Lesser Trefoil
In grassy places. Frequent except in the interior.

| CREICH | LAIRG | ROGART | DORNOCH | GOLSPIE | CLYNE | LOTH | KILDONAN |
| ASSYNT | EDDRACHILLIS | | DURNESS | TONGUE | FARR | | |

Anthyllis L.

A. vulneraria L. (107, 108) Kidney Vetch
Grassy places, cliffs by the sea, on hills on basic rock. Frequent near sea.
—— —— —— DORNOCH GOLSPIE CLYNE LOTH KILDONAN
ASSYNT EDDRACHILLIS DURNESS TONGUE FARR

Lotus L.

L. corniculatus L. (107, 108) Common Birdsfoot-trefoil
Grassy places, dunes, screes and roadsides. Common, widespread.
CREICH LAIRG ROGART DORNOCH GOLSPIE CLYNE LOTH KILDONAN
ASSYNT EDDRACHILLIS DURNESS TONGUE FARR

L. uliginosus Schkuhr. (107, 108) Greater Birdsfoot-trefoil
Moist grassland. Occasional.
—— —— —— CLYNE —— KILDONAN
—— EDDRACHILLIS DURNESS TONGUE FARR

Astragalus L.

A. danicus Retz. (107) Purple Milk-vetch
On sandy turf and dunes. Occasional.
—— —— —— DORNOCH GOLSPIE CLYNE LOTH ——
—— —— —— ——

Oxytropis DC.

O. halleri Bunge (108) Purple Oxytropis
On dunes and sea-cliffs. Rare.
—— —— —— —— —— —— —— ——
—— —— —— —— FARR
Farr (Invernaver, Bettyhill, Farr, Kirtomy, Strathy)

Vicia L.

V. hirsuta (L.) Gray (107) Hairy Tare
Fields and waste places. Occasional.
—— —— —— DORNOCH GOLSPIE CLYNE LOTH KILDONAN
—— —— —— ——

V. tetrasperma (L.) Schreb. (107) Smooth Tare
Grassy places. Rare. No recent records.
CREICH —— —— —— GOLSPIE —— —— ——
—— —— —— ——

77

Creich (Invershin, 1908, G.C.D.)
Golspie (Golspie, 1903, G.C.D.)

V. cracca L. (107, 108) Tufted Vetch
Hedges and roadsides. Frequent.

CREICH	LAIRG	ROGART	DORNOCH	GOLSPIE	CLYNE	LOTH	KILDONAN
ASSYNT	EDDRACHILLIS		DURNESS	TONGUE	FARR		

V. orobus DC. (108) Wood Bitter-vetch
Rocky places near the sea. Rare.

___	___	___	___	___	___	___	___
ASSYNT	EDDRACHILLIS	___		___			

Assynt (Lochinver, Achmelvich, Stoer)
Eddrachillis (Laxford, Kinlochbervie)

V. sylvatica L. (108) Wood Vetch
Dunes and cliffs near the sea. Occasional.

___	___	___	___	___	___	___	___
ASSYNT	___		DURNESS	___	FARR		

Assynt (Clachtoll)
Durness (Kyle of Durness)
Farr (Bettyhill, Farr, Armadale, Melvich)

V. sepium L. (107, 108) Bush Vetch
Roadsides, grassy places. Common.

CREICH	LAIRG	ROGART	DORNOCH	GOLSPIE	CLYNE	LOTH	KILDONAN
ASSYNT	EDDRACHILLIS		DURNESS	TONGUE	FARR		

V. angustifolia L. (107, 108) Narrow-leaved Vetch
Dunes and roadsides. Occasional.

CREICH	___	ROGART	DORNOCH	GOLSPIE	CLYNE	___	KILDONAN
ASSYNT	___		___	TONGUE	FARR		

V. sativa L. (107, 108) Common Vetch
Fields. Occasional.

CREICH	___	___	DORNOCH	___	CLYNE	___	___
ASSYNT	___		___	TONGUE	FARR		

V. lathyroides L. (107) Spring Vetch

___	___	___	DORNOCH	___	___	___	KILDONAN
		___		___	___		

Dornoch (Mound, 1957, M.McC.W.)
Kildonan (Kilpheder, 1962, M.McC.W.)

Lathyrus L.

L. pratensis L. (107, 108) Meadow Vetchling
Roadsides and waste places. Frequent.
CREICH LAIRG ROGART DORNOCH GOLSPIE CLYNE LOTH KILDONAN
ASSYNT EDDRACHILLIS DURNESS TONGUE FARR

L. montanus Bernh. (107, 108) Bitter Vetch
Woods, moorland, grassy banks. Common.
CREICH LAIRG ROGART DORNOCH GOLSPIE CLYNE LOTH KILDONAN
ASSYNT EDDRACHILLIS DURNESS TONGUE FARR

ROSACEAE
Spiraea L.

S. salicifolia L. (107) Bridewort or Willow Spiraea
Damp places amongst scrub. Escape from cultivation. Occasional.
—— LAIRG ROGART DORNOCH GOLSPIE CLYNE —— ——
—— —— —— ——

Filipendula Mill.

F. ulmaria (L.) Maxim. (107, 108) Meadowsweet
Ditches, marshes and wet woods. Common.
CREICH LAIRG ROGART DORNOCH GOLSPIE CLYNE LOTH KILDONAN
ASSYNT EDDRACHILLIS DURNESS TONGUE FARR

Rubus L.

R. chamaemorus L. (107, 108) Cloudberry
Wet peaty places on hills. Common.
CREICH LAIRG ROGART DORNOCH GOLSPIE CLYNE LOTH KILDONAN
ASSYNT EDDRACHILLIS DURNESS TONGUE FARR

R. saxatilis L. (107, 108) Stone Bramble
Rocky and stony places. Common in west.
CREICH —— —— —— —— CLYNE —— ——
ASSYNT EDDRACHILLIS DURNESS TONGUE FARR

R. idaeus L. (107, 108) Raspberry
Woods and hedges. Frequent in east, sparse in north and west.
CREICH LAIRG ROGART DORNOCH GOLSPIE CLYNE LOTH KILDONAN
ASSYNT EDDRACHILLIS DURNESS TONGUE FARR

Sub-genus **Rubus** F. & S.
Section **Suberecti** P.J.Muell.

R. scissus W.C.R.Wats. (107)
Creich (Rosehall, 1959, J.A.)
Dornoch (Dornoch, 1959, J.A.)

R. plicatus Weihe & Nees (107)
Creich (Rosehall & Invershin, 1896, E.S.M. & F.J.H.)

R. fissus Lindl. (107)
Creich (Oykell Bridge, 1897, E.S.M.; Rosehall, 1960, J.A.; Invershin, 1908, G.C.D.)

Section **Triviales** P.J.Muell.

R. sublustris Lees (107)
Creich (Invershin, 1897, E.S.M.)
Dornoch (Mound, 1959, J.A.)
Golspie (Golspie, 1903, G.C.D.)

R. latifolius Bab. (107)
Dornoch (Mound, 1962, M.McC.W.)
Clyne (Brora, 1957, M.McC.W.)

R. purpureicaulis W.C.R.Wats. (107)
Dornoch (Skelbo Street, 1963, J.A.)

Section **Sylvatici** P.J.Muell.

R. nemoralis P.J.Muell. (108)
Eddrachillis (Loch Stack, 1963, J.A.)

R. danicus (Focke) Focke (108)
Eddrachillis (Laxford Bridge, 1962, M.McC.W.)
Tongue (Tongue, 1897, E.S.M. & W.A.S.)

R. villicaulis Koehl ex Weihe & Ness (107, 108)
Abundant in the south and east, local in the north and west.
CREICH LAIRG ROGART DORNOCH GOLSPIE CLYNE LOTH KILDONAN
ASSYNT —— DURNESS TONGUE ——

Section **Appendiculati** (Genev.) Sudre

R. mucronulatus Bor. (107)

80

Abundant in south and east.

CREICH	—	—	DORNOCH	GOLSPIE	CLYNE	LOTH	KILDONAN
—	—		—	—	—	—	

R. radula Weihe ex. Boenn. (107)
Dornoch (Dornoch, 1963, J.A.)
Golspie (Golspie, 1963, J.A.; 1897, E.S.M. & W.A.S.)
Loth (Culgower, 1963, J.A.)

Potentilla L.

P. palustris (L.) Scop. (107, 108) Marsh Cinquefoil
Marshes and bogs. Common in the east, sparse in west.

CREICH	LAIRG	ROGART	DORNOCH	GOLSPIE	CLYNE	LOTH	KILDONAN
ASSYNT	EDDRACHILLIS	DURNESS	TONGUE	FARR			

P. sterilis (L.) Garcke (108) Barren Strawberry
Amongst scrub. Rare.

—	—	—	—	—	—	—	—
—	—	DURNESS	TONGUE	FARR			

P. rupestris L. (107) Rock Cinquefoil
Calcareous cliff ledges. Very rare.

—	—	—	DORNOCH	—			
—	—	—	—				

Dornoch (Cambusmore, 1962, D.A.R.)

P. anserina L. (107, 108) Silverweed
Waste places, dunes, shingle shores. Frequent.

CREICH	LAIRG	ROGART	DORNOCH	GOLSPIE	CLYNE	LOTH	KILDONAN
ASSYNT	EDDRACHILLIS	DURNESS	TONGUE	FARR			

P. crantzii (Crantz) G.Beck ex Fritsch (107, 108) Alpine Cinquefoil
Rock-ledges on hills. Very rare.

—	—	—	—	—	—	—	KILDONAN
ASSYNT	—		DURNESS	—	—		

Kildonan (Ben Griam)
Assynt (Hills round Inchnadamph)
Durness (Ben Hope)

P. erecta (L.) Räusch (107, 108) Tormentil
Heaths, grassland and woods. Common, widespread.

CREICH	LAIRG	ROGART	DORNOCH	GOLSPIE	CLYNE	LOTH	KILDONAN
ASSYNT	EDDRACHILLIS	DURNESS	TONGUE	FARR			

81

P. reptans L. (108) Creeping Cinquefoil
Grassy places. Rare.

——	——	——	——	——	——	——	——

ASSYNT   EDDRACHILLIS   DURNESS —— ——

Sibbaldia L.

S. procumbens L. (107, 108) Sibbaldia or Lesser Cinquefoil
Bare places on mountains. Occasional.

CREICH —— —— —— —— —— —— ——
ASSYNT   EDDRACHILLIS   DURNESS   TONGUE   FARR

Fragaria L.

F. vesca L. (107, 108) Wild Strawberry
Grassy banks and woods. Frequent.

CREICH   LAIRG   ROGART   DORNOCH   GOLSPIE   CLYNE   LOTH   KILDONAN
ASSYNT   EDDRACHILLIS   DURNESS   TONGUE   FARR

Geum L.

G. urbanum L. (107, 108) Wood Avens
Shady places. Occasional in east, sparse in north and west.

CREICH   LAIRG   ROGART   DORNOCH   GOLSPIE   CLYNE   LOTH   KILDONAN
——   EDDRACHILLIS   ——   TONGUE   FARR

G. rivale L. (107, 108) Water Avens
Wet shady places in ditches and woods. Frequent.

CREICH   LAIRG   ROGART   DORNOCH   GOLSPIE   CLYNE   LOTH   ——
ASSYNT   EDDRACHILLIS   DURNESS   TONGUE   FARR

Dryas L.

D. octopetala L. (107, 108) Mountain Avens
Basic rocks on hills and on coastal turf. Frequent in north and west,
very rare in east.

—— —— —— —— —— —— —— KILDONAN
ASSYNT   EDDRACHILLIS   DURNESS   TONGUE   FARR
Kildonan (*Ben Griam*)

Agrimonia L.

A. eupatoria L. (107, 108) Agrimony
Rocky places amongst scrub. Very rare.

—— —— —— DORNOCH ——
—— —— —— —— FARR

82

Dornoch (*Cambusmore*)
Farr (*Altnaharra*)

Alchemilla L.

A. alpina L. (107, 108) Alpine Lady's-mantle
Mountain pastures. Descends to sea-level. Frequent in west, rare in east.

| CREICH | LAIRG | —— | —— | —— | —— | —— | KILDONAN |
| ASSYNT | EDDRACHILLIS | DURNESS | TONGUE | FARR | | | |

A. glaucescens Wallr. (108)
Calcareous grassland. Very rare.

| —— | —— | —— | —— | —— | —— | —— | —— |
| ASSYNT —— | | —— | —— | —— | | | |

Assynt (*Inchnadamph*)

A. filicaulis Buser
sub sp. **vestita** (Buser) M.E.Bradshaw (107, 108)
Grasslands. Frequent.

| CREICH | LAIRG | ROGART | DORNOCH | GOLSPIE | CLYNE | LOTH | KILDONAN |
| ASSYNT | —— | | DURNESS | —— | | —— | |

sub sp. **filicaulis** (107, 108)
Mountain grasslands. Frequent.

| CREICH | —— | —— | —— | —— | CLYNE | —— | KILDONAN |
| ASSYNT | —— | | DURNESS | TONGUE | FARR | | |

A. glomerulans Buser (107)
On rock-ledges. Rare.

| CREICH | —— | —— | —— | —— | —— | —— | —— |
| —— | —— | —— | —— | —— | —— | —— | —— |

A. glabra Neygent. (107, 108)
Grasslands. Frequent.

| CREICH | LAIRG | ROGART | DORNOCH | GOLSPIE | CLYNE | LOTH | KILDONAN |
| ASSYNT | EDDRACHILLIS | | DURNESS | TONGUE | FARR | | |

A. wichurae (Buser) Stéfanss (107, 108)
Mountain grassland. Occasional.

| CREICH | —— | —— | —— | —— | —— | —— | —— |
| ASSYNT | EDDRACHILLIS | | DURNESS | —— | —— | | |

Aphanes L.

A. arvensis L. (107, 108) Parsley Piert

83

Waste places. Occasional.

——   ——   ——   DORNOCH ——   ——   ——   ——
——   EDDRACHILLIS   DURNESS TONGUE   FARR

A. microcarpa (Boiss. & Reut.) Rothm. (107, 108) Slender Parsley Piert
Fields and wasteplaces. Frequent.
CREICH   LAIRG   ROGART   DORNOCH   GOLSPIE   CLYNE   LOTH   KILDONAN
ASSYNT   EDDRACHILLIS   ——   TONGUE   FARR

Acaena Mutis ex L.

A. anserinifolia (J.R. & G.Forst.) Druce (107, 108) Pirri-pirri-bur
Garden escape.
Dornoch (Cambusmore)
Farr (Melvich)

Rosa L.

R. pimpinellifolia L. (107, 108) Burnet Rose
Dunes and sandy heaths. Frequent in all coastal areas.
CREICH   LAIRG   ROGART   DORNOCH   GOLSPIE   CLYNE   LOTH   KILDONAN
ASSYNT   EDDRACHILLIS   DURNESS TONGUE   FARR

×**R. glabra** W-Dod (107)
Clyne (Brora, 1898, E.S.M. & W.A.S.)

×**R. involuta** Sm. (107, 108)
Golspie (Golspie, 1903, G.C.D.)
Assynt (Lochinver, 1890, E.S.M. & F.J.H.)
Durness (Heilam, 1901, E.S.M.)
Farr (Bettyhill, 1910, E.S.M., Armadale & Melvich, 1916, E.S.M.)

×**R. sabinii** Woods (107, 108)
Creich (Inveran, 1959, J.A.)
Assynt (Loch Assynt & Kylesku, 1890, F.J.H. & E.S.M.)
Farr (Invernaver, 1897, E.S.M. & W.A.S.)

R. canina L. var. **globularis** (Franch.) Dum. (108) Dog Rose
Assynt (Lochinver, 1944, A.J.W. & M.S.C.)

R. dumalis Bechst. (107, 108)
Margins of woods, amongst scrub and roadsides. Frequent in east.
CREICH   LAIRG   ROGART   DORNOCH   GOLSPIE   CLYNE   LOTH   KILDONAN
ASSYNT   EDDRACHILLIS   DURNESS TONGUE   FARR

The undermentioned forms have been recorded:

var. **typica** W-Dod (107, 108)
Creich (*Oykell Bridge, 1890, E.S.M., Rosehall & Inveran, 1959, J.A.*)
Rogart (*Rogart, 1959, J.A.*)
Dornoch (*Clashmore, Dornoch, Torboll, Mound, 1959, J.A.*)
Golspie (*Golspie, 1959, J.A.*)
Assynt (*Lochinver, Inchnadamph, Kylesku, 1890, F.J.H. & E.S.M.*)
Durness (*Ben Hope, 1827, R.G.*)
Farr (*Bettyhill, 1889, F.J.H. & E.S.M., 1908, G.C.D., Farr, 1959, J.A.*)

var. **schlimpertii** Hofm.
Assynt (*Lochinver, 1944, A.J.W. & M.S.C.*)

var. **aspernata** (Desegl.) Briggs. (107)
Creich (*Rosehall, 1890, F.J.H. & E.S.M.*)

var. **rueteri** (God.) Cott. (107)
Lairg (*Lairg, 1960, J.A.*)
Dornoch (*Astle, 1959, J.A.*)
Golspie (*Strath Fleet, 1960, J.A.*)

var. **glaucophylla** (Winch) W-Dod (107, 108)
Creich (*Invershin, 1908, G.C.D., Bonar Bridge, 1960, J.A.*)
Kildonan (*Helmsdale, 1960, J.A.*)
Assynt (*Lochinver, 1944, A.J.W. & M.S.C., Inchnadamph & Kylesku, 1890, F.J.H. & E.S.M.*)

var. **subcanina** Chr. (107, 108)
Rogart (*Rogart, 1959, J.A.*)
Golspie (*Mound, 1959, J.A.*)
Farr (*Farr Bay, 1959, J.A.*)

var. **watsoni** (Baker) W-Dod (108)
Assynt (*Lochinver, 1890, E.S.M.*)

var. **bakeri** (Déségl.) W-Dod (107)
Golspie (*Loch Fleet, 1897, E.S.M. & W.A.S.*)
Clyne (*Brora, 1897, E.S.M. & W.A.S.*)

f. **setigera** W-Dod (108)
Assynt (*Lochinver & Achmelvich, 1944, A.J.W. & M.S.C.*)

var. **pruinosa** (Baker) W-Dod (108)
Assynt (*Lochinver, 1897, E.S.M. & W.A.S.*)

R. villosa L. (107, 108)
Wood margins. Occasional.

——— ——— ——— DORNOCH GOLSPIE ——— ——— ———
ASSYNT ——— ——— ——— FARR

var. **mollis** Sm. (107, 108)
Dornoch (Dornoch, 1903, G.C.D.)
Golspie (Golspie, 1903, G.C.D.)
Assynt (Traligill Burn, 1886, A.G.)
Farr (Bettyhill, 1897, W.F.M.)

f. **coerulea** Woods (107, 108)
Dornoch (Mound, 1959, J.A.)
Assynt (Inchnadamph, 1909, E.S.M. & W.A.S.)
Farr (Bettyhill, 1889, W.F.M., Melvich, 1916, E.S.M.)

×**R. schoolbredi** W-Dod (107)
Dornoch (Cuthill, 1959, J.A.)

R. tomentosa Sm. (107, 108)
Margins of woods. Occasional.

CREICH LAIRG ——— ——— GOLSPIE ——— ——— ———
ASSYNT ——— ——— ——— ———

var. **typica** W-Dod (107, 108)
Creich (Invershin, 1908, G.C.D.)
Lairg (Lairg, 1908, G.C.D.)
Assynt (Achmelvich, 1944, A.J.W., Unapool, 1886, A.G., Kylesku, 1908,
E.S.M.)

var. **scabriuscula** Sm. (107)
Golspie (Dunrobin, 1903, G.C.D.)

R. sherardii Davies (107, 108)
Amongst scrub. Frequent.

CREICH LAIRG ROGART DORNOCH GOLSPIE CLYNE LOTH KILDONAN
ASSYNT ——— DURNESS TONGUE FARR

var. **typica** W-Dod (107, 108)
Lairg (Lairg, 1960, J.A.)
Dornoch (Astle, Badnanish, 1960, J.A.)
Golspie (Dunrobin, 1960, J.A.)
Kildonan (Helmsdale, 1960, J.A.)
Assynt (Inchnadamph, 1890, E.S.M.)
Durness (Drocheid Mor, 1960, J.A.)
Farr (Farr Bay, 1959, J.A., Melvich, 1916, E.S.M.)

f. submollis (Ley) W-Dod (107, 108)
Creich (Bonar Bridge, 1959, J.A.)
Dornoch (Clashmore, Camore, 1959, J.A.)
Assynt (Kylesku, 1909, E.S.M. & W.A.S.)

f. pseudomollis (Baker) W-Dod (107, 108)
Dornoch (Mound, 1959, J.A.)
Clyne (Dalcharn, 1960, J.A.)
Loth (Loth, 1960, J.A.)
Durness (Sangomore, 1960, J.A.)

f. uncinata (Lees) W-Dod (107, 108)
Creich (Inveran, 1960, J.A.)
Dornoch (Dornoch, 1959, J.A.)
Tongue (Coldbackie, 1909, E.S.M. & W.A.S.)

var. omissa (Déségl.) W-Dod (107, 108)
Lairg (Lairg, 1960, J.A.)
Dornoch (Astle, 1960, J.A.)
Farr (Farr Bay, 1959, J.A.)

f. resinosoides (Crép.) W-Dod (107, 108)
Creich (Rosehall, 1959, J.A.)
Rogart (Rogart, 1959, J.A.)
Dornoch (Dornoch, 1959, J.A.)
Assynt (Lochinver, 1908, E.S.M.)

var. woodsiana (Groves) W-Dod (107, 108)
Dornoch (Evelix, 1959, J.A.)
Clyne (Tressady, 1960, J.A.)
Farr (Farr Bay, 1959, J.A.)

var. suberecta (Ley) W-Dod
Creich (Oykell Bridge, 1909, E.S.M., Invershin, 1959, J.A.)
Lairg (Lairg, 1960, J.A.)
Rogart (Rogart, 1960, J.A.)
Dornoch (Camore, 1959, J.A.)
Assynt (Lochinver, Inchnadamph, Kylesku, 1909, E.S.M. & W.A.S.)
Farr (Farr Bay, 1959, J.A., Bettyhill, Armadale, 1909, E.S.M.)

f. glabrata Ley (108)
Farr (Bettyhill, 1909, E.S.M.)

R. rubiginosa L. (107) Sweet Briar
Waste places. Escape from cultivation. Rare.

G

Dornoch (*Dornoch, 1959, J.A.*)
Golspie (*Golspie, 1903, G.C.D.*)

Prunus L.

P. spinosa L. (107, 108) Blackthorn
Amongst scrub and wood margins. Occasional in east, rare in north
and west.
CREICH   LAIRG   ROGART   DORNOCH   GOLSPIE   CLYNE   LOTH   KILDONAN
ASSYNT   ———   DURNESS   TONGUE   FARR

P. domestica L. (107) Wild Plum
Introduced. Old record.
Creich (*Rosehall, 1890, F.J.H. & E.S.M.*)

P. avium (L.) L. (107, 108) Wild Cherry or Gean
Woodlands. Occasional. Introduced in west and north.
CREICH   LAIRG   ROGART   DORNOCH   GOLSPIE   CLYNE   LOTH   KILDONAN
ASSYNT   EDDRACHILLIS   ———   ———   FARR

P. padus L. (107, 108) Bird Cherry
Woodlands. Occasional in east, rare in north and west.
CREICH   LAIRG   ROGART   DORNOCH   GOLSPIE   CLYNE   LOTH   KILDONAN
ASSYNT   ———   ———   TONGUE   FARR

Cotoneaster Medic.

C. simonsii Bak. (107) Himalayan Cotoneaster
Escape from gardens.
Dornoch (*Cambusmore*)
Golspie (*Dunrobin*)
Clyne (*Brora*)
Kildonan (*Kildonan*)

C. horizontalis Decne. (107) Wall Cotoneaster
Garden escape. Established on links.
Dornoch (*Dornoch*)

C. microphyllus Wall. ex Lindl. (107) Small-leaved Cotoneaster
Garden escape.
Dornoch (*Cambusmore*)
Kildonan (*Kildonan*)

Crataegus L.

C. monogyna Jacq. (107, 108) Hawthorn
Amongst scrub and in woods. Occasional, probably planted in the north.
CREICH LAIRG ROGART DORNOCH GOLSPIE CLYNE LOTH KILDONAN
ASSYNT EDDRACHILLIS DURNESS TONGUE FARR

Sorbus L.

S. aucuparia L. (107, 108) Rowan
Woods, scrub, mountain rocks. Common, widespread.
CREICH LAIRG ROGART DORNOCH GOLSPIE CLYNE LOTH KILDONAN
ASSYNT EDDRACHILLIS DURNESS TONGUE FARR

S. aria (L.) Crantz sensu lato (107) Common Whitebeam
Planted. Occasional.
CREICH —— —— DORNOCH GOLSPIE CLYNE —— ——
—— —— —— —— —— ——

S. rupicola (Syme) Hedl. (107, 108) Rock Whitebeam
On limestone rocks. Very rare.
—— —— —— DORNOCH —— —— —— ——
ASSYNT —— —— —— —— ——
Dornoch (Cambusmore, 1939, P.M.H., 1962, A.M.G.)
Assynt (Inchnadamph, 1826, R.G.)

CRASSULACEAE
Sedum L.

S. rosea (L.) Scop. (107, 108) Roseroot
Shingle shores, sea-cliffs and mountain cliffs. Frequent in north and west,
rare in east.
CREICH —— —— —— GOLSPIE —— LOTH KILDONAN
ASSYNT EDDRACHILLIS DURNESS TONGUE FARR

S. telephium L. (107) Orpine
Woods. Very rare.
—— —— —— —— GOLSPIE —— ——
—— —— —— —— —— ——

Golspie (Dunrobin)

S. anglicum Huds. (107, 108) English Stonecrop
Sea-cliffs and shingle beaches. Occasional in west, rare in east.
—— —— —— —— GOLSPIE —— —— ——
ASSYNT EDDRACHILLIS DURNESS TONGUE FARR

S. album L. (107, 108) White Stonecrop
Rocks and walls. Introduced, rare.

| | | ROGART | | GOLSPIE | | | |
| ASSYNT | | | | | | | |

S. acre L. (107, 108) Biting Stonecrop or Wall-pepper
Dunes, shingle beaches and rocks. Frequent in coastal areas.

| | | ROGART | DORNOCH | GOLSPIE | CLYNE | LOTH | KILDONAN |
| ASSYNT | EDDRACHILLIS | | DURNESS | TONGUE | FARR | | |

S. forsteranum Sm. (107) Rock Stonecrop
Introduced. Rare.
Creich (Shin)

SAXIFRAGACEAE
Saxifraga L.

S. nivalis L. (107, 108) Alpine Saxifrage
Mountain cliffs, up to 2700 ft. Very rare.

| CREICH | | | | | | | |
| | | | DURNESS | | | | |

Creich (Ben More Assynt, 1962, D.A.R.)
Durness (Meall Horn, 1959, D.A.R.)

S. stellaris L. (107, 108) Starry Saxifrage
Wet rocks on mountains. Frequent in north and west. Descends to
sea-level.

| CREICH | | | | | | LOTH | |
| ASSYNT | EDDRACHILLIS | DURNESS | TONGUE | FARR | | | |

S. tridactylites L. (107, 108) Rue-leaved Saxifrage
Bare sandy places on dunes and on walls. Rare.

| | | | DORNOCH | GOLSPIE | | | |
| | | | | | FARR | | |

Dornoch (Dornoch)
Golspie (Golspie)
Farr (Farr Bay)

S. hypnoides L. (107, 108) Mossy Saxifrage
Wet rock-ledges on mountains. At sea-level in the east. Occasional.

| CREICH | | | DORNOCH | GOLSPIE | | LOTH | |
| ASSYNT | EDDRACHILLIS | DURNESS | TONGUE | FARR | | | |

S. aizoides L. (107, 108) Yellow Saxifrage
Stony ground and rock-ledges on mountains. At sea-level in the north
and west. Frequent in north and west, absent from east.

CREICH —— —— —— —— —— ——
ASSYNT EDDRACHILLIS DURNESS TONGUE FARR

S. oppositifolia L. (107, 108) Purple Saxifrage
Rock-ledges on mountains, stony ground, sea-cliffs and shingle.
Frequent in the north and west. At sea-level on the north coast.
CREICH —— —— —— —— —— KILDONAN
ASSYNT EDDRACHILLIS DURNESS TONGUE FARR

Chrysosplenium L.

C. oppositifolium L. (107, 108) Opposite-leaved Golden-saxifrage
Wet shady places by ditches and streams. Frequent.
CREICH LAIRG ROGART DORNOCH GOLSPIE CLYNE LOTH KILDONAN
ASSYNT EDDRACHILLIS DURNESS TONGUE FARR

PARNASSIACEAE
Parnassia L.

P. palustris L. (107, 108) Grass-of-Parnassus
Marshes, moors and dune-slacks. Frequent.
—— —— —— DORNOCH GOLSPIE —— —— KILDONAN
ASSYNT EDDRACHILLIS DURNESS TONGUE FARR

GROSSULARIACEAE
Ribes L.

R. sylvestre (Lam.) Mert. & Koch (107, 108) Red Currant
Woods. Introduced. Occasional.
CREICH —— ROGART DORNOCH GOLSPIE —— ——
—— —— —— —— TONGUE FARR

R. spicatum Robson (107) Downy Currant or Erect-spiked Red Currant
Introduced.
Kildonan (Kildonan)

R. nigrum L. (107, 108) Black Currant
Woods. Introduced. An escape. Rare.
CREICH —— —— DORNOCH —— —— ——
—— —— —— TONGUE FARR

R. uva-crispa L. (107, 108) Gooseberry
Woods and scrub. Introduced. Occasional.
CREICH —— ROGART DORNOCH GOLSPIE —— —— KILDONAN
ASSYNT —— DURNESS TONGUE ——

DROSERACEAE
Drosera L.

D. rotundifolia L. (107, 108) Round-leaved Sundew
Wet peaty places in moors and bogs. Common, widespread.
CREICH LAIRG ROGART DORNOCH GOLSPIE CLYNE LOTH KILDONAN
ASSYNT EDDRACHILLIS DURNESS TONGUE FARR

D. anglica Huds. (107, 108) Great Sundew
Wet peaty places on moors and in bogs. Common, widespread.
CREICH LAIRG ROGART DORNOCH GOLSPIE CLYNE LOTH KILDONAN
ASSYNT EDDRACHILLIS DURNESS TONGUE FARR

D. × obovata Mert. & Koch (D. rotundifolia × anglica) (108)
Wet peaty places. Occasional.

ASSYNT EDDRACHILLIS —— —— FARR

D. intermedia Hayne (108) Oblong-leaved or Long-leaved Sundew
Wet peaty places. Occasional, mainly in the north and west.

—— —— —— —— —— ——
ASSYNT EDDRACHILLIS DURNESS TONGUE FARR

LYTHRACEAE
Lythrum L.

L. portula (L.) D.A.Webb (107) Water Purslane
Muddy margins of pools. Very rare.
—— —— ROGART DORNOCH —— ——

Rogart (Rogart, 1957, M.McC.W.)
Dornoch (Cuthill, 1958, J.A.)

ELAEAGNACEAE
Hippophaë L.

H. rhamnoides L. (107, 108) Sea-buckthorn
Introduced. Occasional.
—— —— —— —— GOLSPIE —— LOTH ——
—— —— —— —— TONGUE FARR

ONAGRACEAE
Epilobium L.

E. parviflorum Schreb. (107) Hoary Willowherb or Small-flowered
Hairy Willowherb

92

Ditches and margins of ponds. Rare.

CREICH —— —— DORNOCH —— —— —— KILDONAN
—— —— —— —— ——

E. montanum L. (107, 108) Broad-leaved Willowherb
Shady damp places. Common.

CREICH LAIRG ROGART DORNOCH GOLSPIE CLYNE LOTH KILDONAN
ASSYNT EDDRACHILLIS DURNESS TONGUE FARR

E. roseum Schreb. (107) Small-flowered or Pale Willowherb
Garden weed. Rare.

—— —— —— —— —— CLYNE —— ——
—— —— —— —— ——

E. adnatum Griseb. (107) Square-stalked Willowherb
Shady ditches. Rare.

—— —— —— —— —— —— —— KILDONAN
—— —— —— —— ——

E. obscurum Schreb. (107, 108) Short-fruited Willowherb
Damp shady places. Common.

CREICH LAIRG ROGART DORNOCH GOLSPIE CLYNE LOTH KILDONAN
ASSYNT EDDRACHILLIS DURNESS TONGUE FARR

E. palustre L. (107, 108) Marsh Willowherb
Ditches, marshes, margins of ponds. Common, widespread.

CREICH LAIRG ROGART DORNOCH GOLSPIE CLYNE LOTH KILDONAN
ASSYNT EDDRACHILLIS DURNESS TONGUE FARR

E. anagallidifolium Lam. (107, 108) Alpine Willowherb
Wet places on mountains. Occasional on western hills.

CREICH LAIRG —— —— —— —— —— KILDONAN
ASSYNT EDDRACHILLIS DURNESS TONGUE ——

E. alsinifolium Vill. (107, 108) Chickweed Willowherb
Wet places on western mountains. Very occasional.

CREICH LAIRG —— —— —— —— ——
ASSYNT —— DURNESS TONGUE FARR

E. nerterioides Cunn. (108) New Zealand Willowherb
Introduced.
Tongue (Loch Buidhe)
Knocknan rock (Knocknan, 1973, I.A.)

93

Several hybrids have been recorded. Among these are:

E. alsinifolium × E. anagallidifolium
E. alsinifolium × E. obscurum
E. alsinifolium × E. palustre
E. anagallidifolium × E. obscurum
E. anagallidifolium × E. palustre
E. montanum × E. obscurum
E. obscurum × E. palustre

Chamaenerion Adans.

C. angustifolium (L.) Scop. (107, 108) Rosebay Willowherb
Waste places, woodlands, rocks on mountains. Ascends to 1400 ft.
Frequent in south and east, occasional in north and west.
CREICH LAIRG ROGART DORNOCH GOLSPIE CLYNE LOTH KILDONAN
ASSYNT EDDRACHILLIS DURNESS TONGUE FARR

Circaea L.

C. lutetiana L. (108) Enchanter's-nightshade
Shady places in woods. Rare.

| ASSYNT | —— | | DURNESS | —— | —— |

Assynt (Lochinver, Achmelvich)
Durness (Durness)

C. intermedia Ehrh. (107, 108) Upland Enchanter's Nightshade
Shady places amongst rocks and in woods. Rare.

| | | | DORNOCH | GOLSPIE | | | |
| ASSYNT | —— | | —— | —— | FARR | | |

Dornoch (Cambusmore)
Golspie (Dunrobin)
Assynt (Inchnadamph)
Farr (Bettyhill)

HALORAGACEAE
Myriophyllum L.

M. spicatum L. (108) Spiked Water-milfoil
In streams. Rare.

| ASSYNT | —— | | DURNESS | TONGUE | —— |

M. alterniflorum DC. (107, 108) Alternate Water-milfoil

94

In streams. Frequent.

CREICH   LAIRG   ROGART   DORNOCH   GOLSPIE   CLYNE   LOTH   KILDONAN
ASSYNT   EDDRACHILLIS   DURNESS   TONGUE   FARR

HIPPURIDACEAE
Hippuris L.

H. vulgaris L. (107, 108) Mare's-tail
Lochans. Occasional.

——   ——   ROGART   DORNOCH   ——   ——   ——   KILDONAN
——   EDDRACHILLIS   DURNESS   ——   FARR

CALLITRICHACEAE
Callitriche L.

C. stagnalis Scop. (107, 108) Common Water-starwort
Ditches and ponds. Common.

CREICH   LAIRG   ROGART   DORNOCH   GOLSPIE   CLYNE   LOTH   KILDONAN
ASSYNT   EDDRACHILLIS   DURNESS   TONGUE   FARR

C. platycarpa Kütz. (108) Various-leaved Water-starwort
Ditches. Rare.

——   ——   ——   ——   ——   ——   ——   ——
ASSYNT   ——   DURNESS   ——   FARR

C. intermedia Hoffm. (107, 108) Intermediate Water-starwort
sub sp. **hamulata** (Kütz.) Clapham
Ditches, ponds and streams. Occasional.

——   ——   ROGART   ——   ——   CLYNE   ——   ——
ASSYNT   EDDRACHILLIS   ——   ——   FARR

C. hermaphroditica L. (107, 108) Autumnal Water-starwort
Streams. Rare.

——   ——   ——   ——   ——   ——   ——   KILDONAN
——   EDDRACHILLIS   ——   ——   FARR

CORNACEAE
Chamaepericlymenum Hill

C. suecicum (L.) Aschers. & Graebn. (107, 108) Dwarf Cornel
Mountain moors. Frequent in west, rare in east.

CREICH   LAIRG   ——   ——   ——   ——   LOTH   KILDONAN
ASSYNT   EDDRACHILLIS   DURNESS   TONGUE   FARR

ARALIACEAE
Hedera L.

H. helix L. (107, 108) Ivy
Woodlands, hedges, walls, sea-cliffs. Frequent but absent from interior.
CREICH LAIRG ROGART DORNOCH GOLSPIE CLYNE LOTH KILDONAN
ASSYNT EDDRACHILLIS DURNESS TONGUE FARR

UMBELLIFERAE
Hydrocotyle L.

H. vulgaris L. (107, 108) Marsh Pennywort
Bogs and marshes. Frequent.
CREICH LAIRG ROGART DORNOCH GOLSPIE CLYNE LOTH KILDONAN
ASSYNT EDDRACHILLIS DURNESS TONGUE FARR

Sanicula L.

S. europaea L. (107, 108) Sanicle
Woods. Occasional in west, rare in east.
—— —— ROGART —— —— —— —— KILDONAN
ASSYNT EDDRACHILLIS DURNESS TONGUE FARR

Anthriscus Pers.

A. caucalis Bieb. (107) Bur Chervil
Waste places. Casual.
—— —— —— —— GOLSPIE —— —— KILDONAN

Golspie (Golspie)
Kildonan (Helmsdale)

A. sylvestris (L.) Hoffm. (107, 108) Cow Parsley
Fields, roadsides, waste places. Frequent.
CREICH LAIRG ROGART DORNOCH GOLSPIE CLYNE LOTH KILDONAN
ASSYNT EDDRACHILLIS DURNESS TONGUE FARR

Scandix L.

S. pecten-veneris L. (108) Shepherd's-needle
Field. Old record.
Farr (Melvich, 1886, F.J.H.)

96

Myrrhis Mill.

M. odorata (L.) Scop. (107, 108) Sweet Cicely
Roadsides and margins of fields. Occasional in east, rare in north and
west.

| CREICH | —— | ROGART | DORNOCH | GOLSPIE | —— | —— | KILDONAN |
| ASSYNT | —— | | —— | TONGUE | —— | | |

Torilis Adans.

T. japonica (Houtt.) DC. (107, 108) Upright Hedge-parsley
Waste places and roadsides. Occasional in east, very rare in north.

| CREICH | —— | ROGART | DORNOCH | GOLSPIE | CLYNE | LOTH | KILDONAN |
| —— | —— | | DURNESS | —— | | —— | |

Durness (*Balnakeil, 1964, A.G.K.*)

Conium L.

C. maculatum L. (107, 108) Hemlock
Waste places. Occasional.

| —— | —— | —— | DORNOCH | GOLSPIE | CLYNE | —— | KILDONAN |
| —— | —— | | DURNESS | —— | FARR | | |

Apium L.

A. inundatum (L.) Reichb, f. (107) Lesser Marshwort
Marshes. Rare.

| —— | —— | —— | DORNOCH | —— | —— | —— | —— |
| —— | —— | | —— | —— | —— | | |

Dornoch (*Loch Fleet, 1888, J.G., 1962, V.S.S.*)

Carum L.

C. carvi L. (108) Caraway
Introduced. Rare.

| —— | —— | —— | —— | —— | —— | —— | —— |
| —— | —— | | DURNESS | TONGUE | FARR | | |

Conopodium Koch

C. majus (Gouan) Loret (107, 108) Pignut
Fields, banks and woods. Common, widespread.

| CREICH | LAIRG | ROGART | DORNOCH | GOLSPIE | CLYNE | LOTH | KILDONAN |
| ASSYNT | EDDRACHILLIS | | DURNESS | TONGUE | FARR | | |

Pimpinella L.

P. saxifraga L. (107, 108) Burnet-saxifrage
Dry grassy places and dunes. Occasional on the north coast, rare in east.
—— —— —— GOLSPIE CLYNE —— ——
—— —— DURNESS TONGUE FARR

Aegopodium L.

A. podagraria L. (107, 108) Ground-elder or Goutweed
Fields and waste places. Frequent.
CREICH LAIRG ROGART DORNOCH GOLSPIE CLYNE LOTH KILDONAN
ASSYNT EDDRACHILLIS DURNESS TONGUE FARR

Crithmum L.

C. maritimum L. (108) Rock Samphire
On sea-cliffs. Very rare.
—— —— —— —— —— ——
—— —— —— —— FARR
Farr (Strathy Point, Three plants, 1959, M.McC.W.)

Oenanthe L.

O. crocata L. (108) Hemlock Water-dropwort
Marshes. Rare.
—— —— —— —— —— ——
ASSYNT —— —— —— ——
Assynt (Lochinver, 1944, A.J.W.)

Aethusa L.

A. cynapium L. (107) Fool's Parsley
Waste places. Casual.
Golspie (Golspie)

Ligusticum L.

L. scoticum L. (108) Scots Lovage
Sea-cliffs, shingle. Frequent on north and west coasts.
—— —— —— —— —— —— ——
ASSYNT EDDRACHILLIS DURNESS TONGUE FARR

Angelica L.

A. sylvestris L. (107, 108) Wild Angelica

98

Wet woods, damp grassy places and banks, sea-cliffs. Common,
widespread.
CREICH LAIRG ROGART DORNOCH GOLSPIE CLYNE LOTH KILDONAN
ASSYNT EDDRACHILLIS DURNESS TONGUE FARR

Peucedanum L.

P. ostruthium (L.) Koch (107) Masterwort
In old garden.
Loth (*Loth, 1959, M.McC.W.*)

Heracleum L.

H. sphondylium L. (107, 108) Hogweed or Cow Parsnip
Fields, waste places. Common.
CREICH LAIRG ROGART DORNOCH GOLSPIE CLYNE LOTH KILDONAN
ASSYNT EDDRACHILLIS DURNESS TONGUE FARR

Daucus L.

D. carota L. (108) Wild Carrot
Dunes and sandy fields. Frequent on north and west coasts.

ASSYNT EDDRACHILLIS DURNESS TONGUE FARR

EUPHORBIACEAE
Mercurialis L.

M. perennis L. (107, 108) Dog's Mercury
Sandy places. Very rare.
CREICH —— —— —— —— —— —— ——
—— —— —— —— —— FARR

Euphorbia L.

E. helioscopia L. (107, 108) Sun Spurge
Cultivated ground. Frequent in north.
—— —— —— DORNOCH —— —— —— KILDONAN
ASSYNT EDDRACHILLIS DURNESS TONGUE FARR

E. peplus L. (107, 108) Petty Spurge
Cultivated ground. Rare.
—— —— —— DORNOCH —— —— ——
—— EDDRACHILLIS —— —— FARR

E. cyparissias L. (108) Cypress Spurge
Dry grassland. Introduced. Rare.

———	———	———	———	———	———	———	———
———	———		———	TONGUE	FARR		

POLYGONACEAE
Polygonum L.

P. aviculare L. sensu lato (107, 108) Knotgrass
Fields, roadsides, waste places. Common.

CREICH	LAIRG	ROGART	DORNOCH	GOLSPIE	CLYNE	LOTH	KILDONAN
ASSYNT	EDDRACHILLIS		DURNESS	TONGUE	FARR		

P. boreale (Lange) Small (107, 108)
Golspie (*Golspie, 1962, M.McC.W.*)
Durness (*Durness*)

P. viviparum L. (107, 108) Alpine Bistort
Rocky and grassy places on mountains, coastal pastures, at sea-level in the north. Frequent in north and west.

CREICH	LAIRG	ROGART	———	———	———	———	KILDONAN
ASSYNT	EDDRACHILLIS		DURNESS	TONGUE	FARR		

P. amphibium L. (107, 108) Amphibious Bistort
In lochs and ponds. Rare.

———	———	———	DORNOCH	———	CLYNE	———	KILDONAN
ASSYNT	EDDRACHILLIS		DURNESS	———	———		

P. persicaria L. (107, 108) Redshank or Persicaria
Cultivated ground. Common.

CREICH	LAIRG	ROGART	DORNOCH	GOLSPIE	CLYNE	LOTH	KILDONAN
ASSYNT	EDDRACHILLIS		DURNESS	TONGUE	FARR		

P. lapathifolium L. (108) Pale Persicaria
Cultivated ground. Rare.

———	———	———	———	———	———	———	———
ASSYNT	EDDRACHILLIS		DURNESS	———	———		

P. hydropiper L. (108) Common Water-pepper
Wet places. Rare.

———	———	———	———	———	———	———	———
ASSYNT	EDDRACHILLIS		———	———	———		

P. convolvulus L. (107, 108) Black-bindweed
Cultivated fields. Occasional.

P. cuspidatum Sieb. & Zucc. (107, 108) Japanese Knotweed
Garden escape.
Creich (Inveran)
Assynt (Lochinver)

Oxyria Hill

O. digyna (L.) Hill. (108) Mountain Sorrel
Wet rocky places on mountains. At sea-level on north coast. Frequent.

———————   ——————————   ——————— ——————   ————
ASSYNT EDDRACHILLIS DURNESS TONGUE   FARR

Rumex L.

R. acetosella L. sensu lato (107, 108) Sheep's Sorrel
Fields, heaths, waste places. Common, widespread.
CREICH LAIRG ROGART DORNOCH GOLSPIE   CLYNE LOTH   KILDONAN
ASSYNT EDDRACHILLIS DURNESS TONGUE   FARR

R. acetosa L. (107, 108) Common Sorrel
Grassy places. Common, widespread.
CREICH LAIRG ROGART DORNOCH GOLSPIE   CLYNE LOTH   KILDONAN
ASSYNT EDDRACHILLIS DURNESS TONGUE   FARR

R. longifolius DC. (107, 108) Northern Dock or Butter Dock
Damp places. Occasional.
CREICH ——————   —————— ——————   GOLSPIE   CLYNE ——————   KILDONAN
——————   —————   ——————— ——————   ——————   FARR
Farr (Bettyhill, 1889, F.J.H.) Old record.

R. crispus L. (107, 108) Curled Dock
Shingle beaches, dunes, fields, waste places. Common.
CREICH LAIRG ROGART DORNOCH GOLSPIE   CLYNE LOTH   KILDONAN
ASSYNT EDDRACHILLIS DURNESS TONGUE   FARR

R. obtusifolius L. (107, 108) Broad-leaved Dock
Fields, waste places. Common.
CREICH LAIRG ROGART DORNOCH GOLSPIE   CLYNE LOTH   KILDONAN
ASSYNT EDDRACHILLIS DURNESS TONGUE   FARR

R. conglomeratus Murr. (107, 108) Clustered Dock or Sharp Dock
Damp grassy places. Rare.

URTICACEAE
Urtica L.

U. urens L. (107, 108) Small Nettle
Fields, waste places. Occasional in the east.

			DORNOCH	GOLSPIE	CLYNE	——	KILDONAN
ASSYNT	EDDRACHILLIS		DURNESS	TONGUE	FARR		

U. dioica L. (107, 108) Common Nettle or Stinging Nettle
Fields, waste places. Common, widespread.

CREICH	LAIRG	ROGART	DORNOCH	GOLSPIE	CLYNE	LOTH	KILDONAN
ASSYNT	EDDRACHILLIS		DURNESS	TONGUE	FARR		

ULMACEAE
Ulmus L.

U. glabra Huds. (107, 108) Wych Elm
Woodlands. Frequent in the south-east, occasional in north-west.

CREICH	LAIRG	ROGART	DORNOCH	GOLSPIE	CLYNE	LOTH	KILDONAN
ASSYNT	EDDRACHILLIS		DURNESS	TONGUE	FARR		

MYRICACEAE
Myrica L.

M. gale L. (107, 108) Bog Myrtle
Bogs, wet moors. Common, widespread.

CREICH	LAIRG	ROGART	DORNOCH	GOLSPIE	CLYNE	LOTH	KILDONAN
ASSYNT	EDDRACHILLIS		DURNESS	TONGUE	FARR		

BETULACEAE
Betula L.

B. pendula Roth (107, 108) Silver Birch
Woods and heaths on hills. Occasional.

CREICH	LAIRG	ROGART	DORNOCH	GOLSPIE	CLYNE	LOTH	KILDONAN
ASSYNT	EDDRACHILLIS		DURNESS	TONGUE	FARR		

B. pubescens Ehrh. (107, 108) Downy Birch
Woods, heaths in wetter areas. Common, widespread.

CREICH	LAIRG	ROGART	DORNOCH	GOLSPIE	CLYNE	LOTH	KILDONAN
ASSYNT	EDDRACHILLIS		DURNESS	TONGUE	FARR		

B. nana L. (107, 108) Dwarf Birch
Bogs and wet moors. Occasional.

—— LAIRG —— —— —— —— —— ——

—— —— —— TONGUE FARR
Lairg (Ben Hee)
Tongue (Ben Loyal, Ben Tongue)
Farr (Ben Klibreck, Strathy Bog)

hybrid **B. nana** × **pubescens** occurs on Ben Loyal

    Alnus Mill.

A. glutinosa (L.) Gaertn. (107, 108) Alder
Margins of lakes and streams. Common.
CREICH LAIRG ROGART DORNOCH GOLSPIE CLYNE LOTH KILDONAN
ASSYNT EDDRACHILLIS DURNESS TONGUE FARR

    CORYLACEAE
    Carpinus L.

C. betulus L. (107, 108) Hornbeam
Introduced.
Golspie (Dunrobin)
Tongue (Borgie)
Farr (Melvich)

    Corylus L.

C. avellana L. (107, 108) Hazel
Woods, scrub, hedges. Common.
CREICH LAIRG ROGART DORNOCH GOLSPIE CLYNE LOTH KILDONAN
ASSYNT EDDRACHILLIS DURNESS TONGUE FARR

    FAGACEAE
    Fagus L.

F. sylvatica L. (107, 108) Beech
Woods. Frequent in south-east, sparse in north and west. Introduced.
CREICH LAIRG ROGART DORNOCH GOLSPIE CLYNE LOTH KILDONAN
ASSYNT EDDRACHILLIS DURNESS TONGUE FARR

    Castanea Mill.

C. sativa Mill. (107) Sweet Chestnut
In woods. Introduced. Rare.

H

CREICH —— —— DORNOCH GOLSPIE —— —— ——

Quercus L.

Q. robur L. (107, 108) Pedunculate Oak
In woods. Introduced in north. Occasional.
CREICH —— —— DORNOCH GOLSPIE CLYNE —— KILDONAN
ASSYNT —— DURNESS —— FARR

Q. petraea (Mattuschka) Liebl. (107, 108) Sessile Oak
Woods in the south-east, frequent, sparse in the north. Often planted.
CREICH LAIRG ROGART DORNOCH GOLSPIE CLYNE LOTH KILDONAN
ASSYNT EDDRACHILLIS DURNESS TONGUE FARR

SALICACEAE
Populus L.

P. tremula L. (107, 108) Aspen
Woods, rocky places on heaths and ravines and sea-cliffs. Common.
CREICH LAIRG ROGART DORNOCH GOLSPIE CLYNE LOTH KILDONAN
ASSYNT EDDRACHILLIS DURNESS TONGUE FARR

P. alba L. (107, 108) White Poplar
Introduced.
Golspie (Golspie, Dunrobin)
Farr (Altnaharra)

P. nigra agg. (107, 108) Black Poplar
Introduced.
Creich (Rosehall)
Rogart (Rogart)
Assynt (Lochinver)
Tongue (Tongue)

Salix L.

S. pentandra L. (107, 108) Bay Willow
Introduced. Usually near houses.
CREICH —— —— —— —— —— ——
ASSYNT —— DURNESS TONGUE FARR

S. alba L. (107, 108) White Willow
Introduced. Very occasional.
—— —— —— —— GOLSPIE —— —— ——
—— —— DURNESS ——

S. fragilis L. (107, 108) Crack Willow
Introduced, occasional.
CREICH —— —— DORNOCH GOLSPIE CLYNE —— ——
ASSYNT EDDRACHILLIS ——   ——

S. purpurea L. (107, 108) Purple Willow
Introduced. Very occasional.
CREICH —— —— —— —— —— ——
ASSYNT —— DURNESS —— —— ——

S. viminalis L. (107, 108) Osier
Wet places. Frequently planted round houses. Absent from interior.
CREICH LAIRG ROGART DORNOCH GOLSPIE CLYNE LOTH KILDONAN
ASSYNT EDDRACHILLIS DURNESS TONGUE FARR

S. caprea L. (107, 108) Goat Willow
Woods. Occasional in the south-east; sparse in the north.
CREICH LAIRG ROGART DORNOCH GOLSPIE CLYNE LOTH KILDONAN
ASSYNT EDDRACHILLIS DURNESS TONGUE FARR

S. cinerea L. Grey Willow or Common Sallow
sub sp. **atrocinerea** (Brot) Silva & Sobrinho (107, 108)
Woods and scrub. Common.
CREICH LAIRG ROGART DORNOCH GOLSPIE CLYNE LOTH KILDONAN
ASSYNT EDDRACHILLIS DURNESS TONGUE FARR

S. aurita L. (107, 108) Eared Willow
Damp woods and moorland. Common, widespread.
CREICH LAIRG ROGART DORNOCH GOLSPIE CLYNE LOTH KILDONAN
ASSYNT EDDRACHILLIS DURNESS TONGUE FARR

S. nigricans Sm. (107, 108) Dark-leaved Willow
Wet places. Rare.

—— EDDRACHILLIS —— —— ——
Eddrachillis (Scourie)

S. phylicifolia L. (107, 108) Tea-leaved Willow
Wet rocks on mountains. Rare.
—— —— ROGART —— —— —— ——
—— DURNESS TONGUE FARR

S. repens L. (107, 108) Creeping Willow
sub sp. **repens.** Damp and wet heaths. Common.
sub sp. **argentea** (Sm.) G. & A. Camus. Dune slacks and rocky heaths
near the sea. Common.

CREICH LAIRG ROGART DORNOCH GOLSPIE CLYNE LOTH KILDONAN
ASSYNT EDDRACHILLIS DURNESS TONGUE FARR

S. lapponum L. (108) Downy Willow
Wet rocks on mountains. Rare.

_____ _____ _____ _____ _____ _____ _____
ASSYNT —— DURNESS —— FARR

S. myrsinites L. (107, 108) Whortle-leaved Willow
Basic rocks on mountains. Rare.

_____ _____ _____ _____ _____ _____ —— KILDONAN
ASSYNT —— DURNESS —— ——

S. herbacea L. (107, 108) Dwarf Willow or Least Willow
Bare ground and rock-ledges on mountains. Frequent on higher hills.
CREICH LAIRG ROGART —— _____ _____ —— KILDONAN
ASSYNT EDDRACHILLIS DURNESS TONGUE FARR

S. reticulata L. (108) Net-leaved or Reticulate Willow
Mountain screes. Very rare.

_____ _____ _____ _____ _____ _____ _____
—— —— DURNESS ——
Durness (_Ben Hope, 1833, J.M., 1957, R.E.C.F._)

ERICACEAE
Loiseleuria Desv.

L. procumbens (L.) Desv. (107, 108) Trailing Azalea or Loiseleuria
On dry stony places on mountain moors. From 700 ft near the north
coast to 2600 ft on Ben Hope. Chiefly in the north and west. Frequent.
CREICH LAIRG —— _____ _____ CLYNE —— KILDONAN
ASSYNT EDDRACHILLIS DURNESS TONGUE FARR

    Arctostaphylos Adans.

A. uva-ursi (L.) Spreng. (107, 108) Bearberry
Dry rocky places on mountains and heaths. Descends to sea-level on
north coast. Common.
CREICH LAIRG —— _____ _____ —— —— KILDONAN
ASSYNT EDDRACHILLIS DURNESS TONGUE FARR

    Arctous (A. Gray) Nied.

A. alpinus (L.) Nied. (107, 108) Alpine Bearberry or Black Bearberry
On barren mountain tops. Frequent on hills in the north and west.

Descends to 400 ft on the north coast.

CREICH LAIRG —— —— —— CLYNE —— KILDONAN
ASSYNT EDDRACHILLIS DURNESS TONGUE FARR

Calluna Salisb.

C. vulgaris (L.) Hull (107, 108) Heather
On heaths, moors, woods and dunes. Common, widespread.

CREICH LAIRG ROGART DORNOCH GOLSPIE CLYNE LOTH KILDONAN
ASSYNT EDDRACHILLIS DURNESS TONGUE FARR

Erica L.

E. tetralix L. (107, 108) Cross-leaved Heath
Damp heaths, moors and woods. Common, widespread.

CREICH LAIRG ROGART DORNOCH GOLSPIE CLYNE LOTH KILDONAN
ASSYNT EDDRACHILLIS DURNESS TONGUE FARR

E. cinerea L. (107, 108) Bell Heather
Dry heaths and moors. Common, widespread.

CREICH LAIRG ROGART DORNOCH GOLSPIE CLYNE LOTH KILDONAN
ASSYNT EDDRACHILLIS DURNESS TONGUE FARR

Vaccinium L.

V. vitis-idaea L. (107, 108) Cowberry
Woods and heaths. Common.

CREICH LAIRG ROGART DORNOCH GOLSPIE CLYNE LOTH KILDONAN
ASSYNT EDDRACHILLIS DURNESS TONGUE FARR

V. myrtillus L. (107, 108) Bilberry or Blaeberry
Woods, moors and mountains. Common, widespread.

CREICH LAIRG ROGART DORNOCH GOLSPIE CLYNE LOTH KILDONAN
ASSYNT EDDRACHILLIS DURNESS TONGUE FARR

V. uliginosum L. (107, 108) Bog Bilberry or Bog Whortleberry
On high wet moors. Mainly in the north and west. Occasional.

CREICH LAIRG ROGART —— —— —— —— KILDONAN
ASSYNT EDDRACHILLIS DURNESS TONGUE FARR

V. oxycoccus L. (107) Cranberry
In bogs. Very rare.

CREICH —— —— —— —— —— —— ——
—— —— —— —— —— —— ——

Creich (Oykell Bridge, 1909, E.S.M.)

PYROLACEAE
Pyrola L.

P. minor L. (107, 108) Common Wintergreen
Cliff-ledges on hills and in woods. Rare.
CREICH —— —— —— GOLSPIE —— —— ——
—— —— DURNESS TONGUE —— ——
Creich (Ben More Assynt, 1962, D.A.R.)
Golspie (Golspie, 1888, J.G., 1959, J.A.)
Durness (Ben Hope, 1900, E.S.M.)
Tongue (Rhi-Tongue, 1886, A.G.; Ben Loyal, 1887, J.H.)

P. media Sw. (107, 108) Intermediate Wintergreen
Rocky places on heaths. Rare.
CREICH —— —— —— —— —— KILDONAN
—— —— —— —— ——
Creich (Invershin, 1887, W.C., 1888, J.G.)
Kildonan (Ord, 1959, J.A.)
Farr (Strath Vagastie, 1899, W.F.M.)

P. rotundifolia L. (108) Round-leaved Wintergreen
Cliff-ledges on hills. Very rare.
—— —— —— —— —— ——
—— —— DURNESS —— —— ——
Durness (Ben Hope, 1900, E.S.M., 1959, J.A.)

Orthilia Raf.

O. secunda (L.) House (107) Serrated Wintergreen
Pine-woods and rock-ledges on hills. Rare.
—— —— —— DORNOCH GOLSPIE CLYNE —— KILDONAN
Dornoch (Cambusmore, 1962, A.McG.S.)
Golspie (Ben Braghie, 1888, J.G.)
Clyne (Loch Brora, 1962, J.A.)
Kildonan (Achentoul, 1962, A.McG.S.)

Moneses Salisb.

M. uniflora (L.) A. Gray (107) One-flowered Wintergreen
In pine woods. Very rare.
—— —— —— —— —— GOLSPIE —— —— ——
—— —— —— —— ——
Golspie (Balblair, 1890, F.C.C., 1897, E.S.M. & F.J.H., 1923, G.C.D., 1960, J.A.; Mound, 1900, T.J.F.)

EMPETRACEAE
Empetrum L.

E. nigrum L. (107, 108) Crowberry
On moors. Common.
CREICH LAIRG ROGART DORNOCH GOLSPIE CLYNE LOTH KILDONAN
ASSYNT EDDRACHILLIS DURNESS TONGUE FARR

E. hermaphroditum Hagerup (107, 108) Mountain Crowberry
Mountain moors, mainly in the north and west, at the highest altitudes.
Frequent.
CREICH LAIRG —— —— —— CLYNE —— KILDONAN
ASSYNT EDDRACHILLIS DURNESS TONGUE FARR

PLUMBAGINACEAE
Armeria Willd.

A. maritima (Mill.) Willd. (107, 108) Thrift
sub sp. **maritima**
Salt-marshes, coastal pastures, sea-cliffs and on mountains. Ascends to
3000 ft. Frequent.
CREICH —— —— DORNOCH GOLSPIE —— —— KILDONAN
ASSYNT EDDRACHILLIS DURNESS TONGUE FARR

PRIMULACEAE
Primula L.

P. scotica Hook. (108) Scottish Primrose
Pastures by the sea. All along the north coast. Occasional.
—— —— —— —— ——
—— —— —— DURNESS TONGUE FARR

P. veris L. (107, 108) Cowslip
Sandy pastures by the sea, occasional in north, very rare in the east.
—— —— DORNOCH —— —— ——
ASSYNT —— —— DURNESS TONGUE FARR

P. vulgaris Huds. (107, 108) Primrose
Woods and banks. Common.
CREICH LAIRG ROGART DORNOCH GOLSPIE CLYNE LOTH KILDONAN
ASSYNT EDDRACHILLIS DURNESS TONGUE FARR

Lysimachia L.

L. nemorum L. (107, 108) Yellow Pimpernel
Woods and banks. Common.

CREICH LAIRG ROGART DORNOCH GOLSPIE CLYNE LOTH KILDONAN
ASSYNT EDDRACHILLIS DURNESS TONGUE FARR

L. vulgaris L. (107) Yellow Loosestrife
Near old garden. An escape.
Dornoch (Badnanish)

Trientalis L.

T. europaea L. (107, 108) Chickweed Wintergreen
Woods and moorland. Widely but sparsely distributed. Frequent.

CREICH LAIRG ROGART DORNOCH GOLSPIE CLYNE LOTH KILDONAN
ASSYNT —— DURNESS TONGUE FARR

Anagallis L.

A. tenella (L.) L. (108) Bog Pimpernel
In bogs, marshy area and stream sides. Occasional.

—— —— —— —— ——
ASSYNT EDDRACHILLIS DURNESS TONGUE FARR

A. arvensis L. (107) Scarlet Pimpernel
In fields. Rare.

CREICH —— —— —— —— CLYNE —— ——
—— —— —— —— ——
Creich (Rosehall)
Clyne (Brora)

Glaux L.

G. maritima L. (107, 108) Sea-milkwort
Salt marshes, sandy and stony shores. Frequent.

—— —— —— DORNOCH GOLSPIE —— —— ——
ASSYNT EDDRACHILLIS DURNESS TONGUE FARR

OLEACEAE
Fraxinus L.

F. excelsior L. (107, 108) Ash
Woodlands. Frequent in east, sparse (introduced) in north-west.

CREICH LAIRG ROGART DORNOCH GOLSPIE CLYNE LOTH KILDONAN
ASSYNT EDDRACHILLIS DURNESS TONGUE FARR

110

Ligustrum L.

L. vulgare L. (107, 108) Wild Privet
Introduced.

CREICH —— ROGART —— GOLSPIE —— LOTH ——
ASSYNT —— —— TONGUE FARR

GENTIANACEAE
Centaurium Hill

C. littorale (D. Turner) Gilmour (107) Seaside Centaury
Damp sandy places by the sea. Very rare.

—— —— —— DORNOCH —— —— —— ——
—— —— —— —— ——

Dornoch (Dornoch Links, south shore of Loch Fleet)

Gentianella Moench

G. campestris (L.) Börner (107, 108) Field Gentian
Grassland and dunes. Frequent by the sea.

CREICH LAIRG ROGART DORNOCH GOLSPIE CLYNE LOTH KILDONAN
ASSYNT EDDRACHILLIS DURNESS TONGUE FARR

G. amarella (L.) Börner. Autumn Gentian or Felwort
Dunes and sandy pastures by the sea.
sub sp. **druceana** Pritchard (107, 108)

—— —— —— DORNOCH GOLSPIE CLYNE —— ——
—— —— —— —— TONGUE FARR
sub sp. **septentrionalis** (Druce) Pritchard (107, 108)

CREICH —— —— —— —— —— —— ——
ASSYNT EDDRACHILLIS DURNESS TONGUE FARR

G. pulchra Brummet & Heywood (108)

—— —— —— —— —— ——
ASSYNT —— —— —— ——

MENYANTHACEAE
Menyanthes L.

M. trifoliata L. (107, 108) Bogbean
Marshes, bogs and lake-margins. Common.

CREICH LAIRG ROGART DORNOCH GOLSPIE CLYNE LOTH KILDONAN
ASSYNT EDDRACHILLIS DURNESS TONGUE FARR

BORAGINACEAE
Symphytum L.

S. officinale L. (107, 108) Common Comfrey
Wet grassy places and ditches. Occasional.

—— —— —— DORNOCH GOLSPIE CLYNE LOTH KILDONAN
ASSYNT EDDRACHILLIS —— TONGUE FARR

S. tuberosum L. (107) Tuberous Comfrey
Roadside. Rare.

—— —— —— —— —— —— KILDONAN

Kildonan (Kinbrace)

Pentaglottis Tausch

P. sempervirens (L.) Tausch (107, 108) Green Alkanet
Hedges and roadsides. Occasional.

—— LAIRG —— —— GOLSPIE —— LOTH KILDONAN
ASSYNT —— —— TONGUE ——

Lycopsis L.

L. arvensis L. (107, 108) Bugloss
In cultivated fields. Frequent.

—— —— —— DORNOCH GOLSPIE CLYNE LOTH KILDONAN
ASSYNT EDDRACHILLIS DURNESS TONGUE FARR

Myosotis L.

M. scorpioides L. (107, 108) Water Forget-me-not
In wet places, ditches, ponds. Frequent.

CREICH LAIRG ROGART DORNOCH GOLSPIE CLYNE LOTH KILDONAN
ASSYNT EDDRACHILLIS DURNESS TONGUE FARR

M. secunda A. Murr. (107, 108) Creeping Forget-me-not
In wet peaty places. Common.

CREICH LAIRG ROGART DORNOCH GOLSPIE CLYNE LOTH KILDONAN
ASSYNT EDDRACHILLIS DURNESS TONGUE FARR

M. caespitosa K. F. Schultz (107, 108) Tufted Forget-me-not
In marshes and ponds. Frequent but absent from the interior.

CREICH LAIRG ROGART DORNOCH GOLSPIE CLYNE LOTH KILDONAN
ASSYNT EDDRACHILLIS DURNESS TONGUE FARR

112

M. arvensis (L.) Hill (107, 108) Field Forget-me-not
In cultivated fields, dunes and waste places. Frequent.
CREICH LAIRG ROGART DORNOCH GOLSPIE CLYNE LOTH KILDONAN
ASSYNT EDDRACHILLIS DURNESS TONGUE FARR

M. discolor Pers. (107, 108) Changing Forget-me-not or
Yellow and Blue Forget-me-not
In dry bare waste places. Common.
CREICH LAIRG ROGART DORNOCH GOLSPIE CLYNE LOTH KILDONAN
ASSYNT EDDRACHILLIS DURNESS TONGUE FARR

M. ramosissima Rochel (107) Early Forget-me-not
Waste places. Rare.
—— —— —— —— GOLSPIE CLYNE —— ——
—— —— —— —— —— ——

Golspie (Golspie)
Clyne (Brora)

Mertensia Roth

M. maritima (L.) Gray (107, 108) Northern Shore-wort or Oyster Plant
On coastal shingle. Rare. Decreasing.
—— —— —— —— GOLSPIE —— LOTH KILDONAN
ASSYNT EDDRACHILLIS —— TONGUE FARR
Golspie (Dunrobin, 1903, G.C.D., very scarce, now extinct)
Loth (Loth, 1965, M.M., one plant)
Kildonan (Helmsdale, 1845, D.R., now extinct)
Assynt (Inverkirkaig, 1886, A.G.; Clachtoll, 1956, J.A.)
Eddrachillis (Sandwood, 1919, now extinct)
Tongue (Skerray, 1956, J.A., two plants)
Farr (Kirtomy, 1895, E.S.M. & F.J.H., 1954, J.A., now extinct)

CONVOLVULACEAE
Convolvulus L.

C. arvensis L. (107) Field Bindweed
Recorded by H. C. Watson without locality.

Calystegia R. Br.

C. sepium (L.) R. Br. (107, 108) Hedge Bindweed or Larger Bindweed
Hedges and waste places. Occasional.
—— —— —— DORNOCH —— —— —— KILDONAN
ASSYNT —— —— —— FARR

113

C. silvatica (Kit.) Griseb. (107) Large Bindweed
Hedges. Occasional.

—	LAIRG	—	—	GOLSPIE	CLYNE	LOTH	KILDONAN

C. pulchra Brummitt & Heywood (108) Hairy Bindweed
Assynt (Inchnadamph)

SOLANACEAE
Lycium L.

L. chinense Mill. (108) China Teaplant or Duke of Argyll's Tea-plant
On wall at roadside. An escape.
Durness (Balnakiel)

Hyoscyamus L.

H. niger L. (107) Henbane
In waste ground. Casual.
Golspie (Golspie, 1898, E.S.M. & W.A.S.)

Solanum L.

S. dulcamara L. (107, 108) Bittersweet
On waste ground. An escape.
Creich (Bonar Bridge, 1962, J.A.)
Assynt (Lochinver, 1944)
Farr (Bettyhill, 1897, E.S.M.)

SCROPHULARIACEAE
Verbascum L.

V. thapsus L. (107) Great Mullein or Aaron's Rod
On waste ground. Casual.
Golspie (Golspie, 1888, J.G., 1898, E.S.M. & W.A.S.)

Linaria Mill.

L. vulgaris Mill. (107, 108) Common Toadflax
On railway banks. Occasional.

CREICH	LAIRG	ROGART	DORNOCH	GOLSPIE	—	—	KILDONAN
					FARR		

Cymbalaria Hill

C. muralis Gaertn., Mey. & Scherb. (107, 108) Ivy-leaved Toadflax
On walls. Garden escape.

114

—— —— —— GOLSPIE —— —— —— ——
—— EDDRACHILLIS —— —— FARR
Golspie (Golspie, Little Ferry)
Eddrachillis (Scourie)
Farr (Melvich)

Scrophularia L.

S. nodosa L. (107, 108) Common Figwort
Damp woods, banks and ditches. Occasional in south and east. Very
local in north and west.
CREICH LAIRG ROGART DORNOCH GOLSPIE CLYNE LOTH KILDONAN
ASSYNT EDDRACHILLIS —— —— FARR

Mimulus L.

M. guttatus DC. (107, 108) Monkeyflower
Banks of streams. Introduced. Established in many localities. Frequent.
CREICH LAIRG ROGART DORNOCH GOLSPIE CLYNE LOTH KILDONAN
ASSYNT EDDRACHILLIS DURNESS TONGUE FARR

M. luteus L. (107, 108) Blood-drop-emlets
Banks of streams. Introduced. Much less frequent than *M. guttatus*.
—— LAIRG —— —— —— —— LOTH KILDONAN
ASSYNT —— DURNESS TONGUE FARR

M. moschatus Dougl. ex Lindl. (107, 108) Musk
Banks of streams and ditches. Introduced. Occasional, near gardens.
CREICH LAIRG ROGART —— GOLSPIE —— —— KILDONAN
—— —— DURNESS TONGUE FARR

Erinus L.

E. alpinus L. (108) Fairy Foxglove
Introduced.
Farr (Bettyhill, 1959, D.P.Y.)

Digitalis L.

D. purpurea L. (107, 108) Foxglove
In woods, heaths and banks. Common, widespread.
CREICH LAIRG ROGART DORNOCH GOLSPIE CLYNE LOTH KILDONAN
ASSYNT EDDRACHILLIS DURNESS TONGUE FARR

Veronica L.

V. beccabunga L. (107, 108) Brooklime

115

In ditches and streams. Occasional.

			DORNOCH	GOLSPIE	CLYNE	LOTH	KILDONAN
ASSYNT	EDDRACHILLIS		DURNESS	——	FARR		

V. anagallis-aquatica L. (108) Blue Water-speedwell
In streams. Rare.

——	——		DURNESS	——	——		

Durness (Balnakeil, Eriboll)

V. scutellata L. (107, 108) Marsh Speedwell
Wet places, ditches, ponds and bogs. Frequent.

CREICH	LAIRG	ROGART	DORNOCH	GOLSPIE	CLYNE	LOTH	KILDONAN
ASSYNT	——		DURNESS	TONGUE	FARR		

V. officinalis L. (107, 108) Heath Speedwell
Dunes, heaths and woods. Common, widespread.

CREICH	LAIRG	ROGART	DORNOCH	GOLSPIE	CLYNE	LOTH	KILDONAN
ASSYNT	EDDRACHILLIS		DURNESS	TONGUE	FARR		

V. chamaedrys L. (107, 108) Germander Speedwell
Woods, pastures, dunes and roadsides. Common, widespread.

CREICH	LAIRG	ROGART	DORNOCH	GOLSPIE	CLYNE	LOTH	KILDONAN
ASSYNT	EDDRACHILLIS		DURNESS	TONGUE	FARR		

V. serpyllifolia L. (107, 108) Thyme-leaved Speedwell
sub sp. **serpyllifolia**
Grasslands and waste places. Common, widespread.

CREICH	LAIRG	ROGART	DORNOCH	GOLSPIE	CLYNE	LOTH	KILDONAN
ASSYNT	EDDRACHILLIS		DURNESS	TONGUE	FARR		

sub sp. **humifusa** (Dickson) Syme
Damp places on mountains. Occasional.

CREICH	——	——	——	——	——		KILDONAN
ASSYNT	EDDRACHILLIS		DURNESS	TONGUE	FARR		

V. arvensis L. (107, 108) Wall Speedwell
Cultivated fields. Common.

CREICH	LAIRG	ROGART	DORNOCH	GOLSPIE	CLYNE	LOTH	KILDONAN
ASSYNT	EDDRACHILLIS		DURNESS	TONGUE	FARR		

V. hederifolia L. (107, 108) Ivy-leaved Speedwell
In waste places. Occasional.

			DORNOCH	——	——		KILDONAN
ASSYNT	——		——	——	FARR		

116

V. persica Poir. (107, 108) Common Field-speedwell or
Buxbaum's Speedwell
In cultivated fields. Frequent.
CREICH LAIRG ROGART DORNOCH GOLSPIE CLYNE LOTH KILDONAN
ASSYNT EDDRACHILLIS DURNESS TONGUE FARR

V. polita Fr. (108) Grey Field-speedwell
Waste ground. Rare.

—— —— —— —— —— —— ——
—— —— DURNESS —— FARR

V. agrestis L. (107, 108) Green Field-speedwell
Cultivated ground. Occasional.
—— LAIRG —— DORNOCH —— —— —— KILDONAN
ASSYNT EDDRACHILLIS DURNESS TONGUE FARR

V. filiformis Sm. (107, 108) Slender Speedwell
At roadsides amongst grass. Casual, rare.
—— —— DORNOCH —— —— —— KILDONAN
ASSYNT —— —— TONGUE FARR

Pedicularis L.

P. palustris L. (107, 108) Marsh Lousewort or Red-rattle
In marshes. Common.
CREICH LAIRG ROGART DORNOCH GOLSPIE CLYNE LOTH KILDONAN
ASSYNT EDDRACHILLIS DURNESS TONGUE FARR

P. sylvatica L. (107, 108) Lousewort
Damp heaths and moors. Common, widespread.
CREICH LAIRG ROGART DORNOCH GOLSPIE CLYNE LOTH KILDONAN
ASSYNT EDDRACHILLIS DURNESS TONGUE FARR

Rhinanthus L.

R. serotinus (Schönh) Oborny (108) Greater Yellow-rattle
Farr (*Bettyhill, 1923, G.C.D.*)

R. minor L. (107, 108) Yellow-rattle
Grassy places. Common.
CREICH LAIRG ROGART DORNOCH GOLSPIE CLYNE LOTH KILDONAN
ASSYNT EDDRACHILLIS DURNESS TONGUE FARR
sub sp. **stenophyllus** (Schur.) O. Schwarz (107, 108)
Damp grassy places. Common.

117

CREICH LAIRG ROGART DORNOCH GOLSPIE CLYNE LOTH KILDONAN
ASSYNT EDDRACHILLIS DURNESS TONGUE FARR

sub sp. **monticola** (Sterneck) O. Schwarz (107, 108)
Grassy places. Common.

CREICH —— —— DORNOCH GOLSPIE —— —— ——
ASSYNT —— DURNESS TONGUE FARR

sub sp. **borealis** (Sterneck) Druce. (107, 108)
Grassy places on hills, at sea-level on north coast. Occasional.

CREICH —— —— —— —— —— —— KILDONAN
ASSYNT EDDRACHILLIS DURNESS TONGUE FARR

Melampyrum L.

M. pratense L. (107, 108) Common Cow-wheat
sub sp. **pratense** var hians Druce.
Woods and heaths. Common, widespread.

CREICH LAIRG ROGART DORNOCH GOLSPIE CLYNE LOTH KILDONAN
ASSYNT EDDRACHILLIS DURNESS TONGUE FARR

Euphrasia L.

E. officinalis L. (107, 108) Eyebright
Heaths, moors and screes. Common.

CREICH LAIRG ROGART DORNOCH GOLSPIE CLYNE LOTH KILDONAN
ASSYNT EDDRACHILLIS DURNESS TONGUE FARR

E. micrantha × nemorosa Durness.

E. scottica Wettst. (107, 108)
On wet moors. Not uncommon in the north and west, rare in the east.
Ascends to 2000 ft on Ben More.

CREICH LAIRG —— DORNOCH —— —— —— ——
ASSYNT EDDRACHILLIS DURNESS TONGUE FARR

E. frigida Pugsl. (107, 108)
Rocky places on mountains. Ascends to 2500 ft on Ben More. Rare.

CREICH —— —— —— —— —— —— ——
ASSYNT —— DURNESS TONGUE FARR

Creich (Ben More)
Assynt (Craig Liath)
Durness (Ben Hope)
Tongue (Ben Loyal)
Farr (Ben Klibreck)

E. frigida × micrantha. Ben Loyal
E. frigida × scottica. Ben Hope

E. foulaensis Townsend ex Wettst. (107, 108)
Coastal pastures and salt marshes. Occasional.

——	——	——	DORNOCH	——	——	——	——
ASSYNT	EDDRACHILLIS		DURNESS	TONGUE	FARR		

Dornoch (Dornoch, Loch Fleet)
Eddrachillis (Handa)
Durness (Smoo)
Tongue (Kyle of Tongue)
Farr (Invernaver, Bettyhill, Farr, Strathy & Melvich)

E. foulaensis × marshallii. Bettyhill
E. foulaensis × nemorosa. Melness

E. rotundifolia Pugsl. (108)
Grassy sea-cliffs. Very rare.

——	EDDRACHILLIS	DURNESS	TONGUE	FARR

Eddrachillis (Sandwood)
Durness (Balnakeil)
Tongue (Scullomie)
Farr (Port Skerra)

E. marshallii Pugsl. (108)
Grassy places on sea-cliffs. Occasional on north coast, sparse on west.

ASSYNT	EDDRACHILLIS	DURNESS	TONGUE	FARR

E. marshallii × micrantha. Eddrachillis, Durness and Tongue
E. marshallii × brevipila. Durness and Farr
E. marshallii × nemorosa. Tongue and Farr

E. curta (Fr.) Wettst. (107, 108)
Pastures near the sea and on mountain slopes. Occasional.

——	——	——	DORNOCH	——	——	——	——
ASSYNT	——			TONGUE	FARR		

E. curta × brevipila. Tongue and Dornoch

E. nemorosa (Pers.) Wallr. (107, 108)
Pastures, dunes, heaths. Occasional.

——	——	——	DORNOCH	GOLSPIE	CLYNE	——	——
——	EDDRACHILLIS		DURNESS	TONGUE	FARR		

E. nemorosa × brevipila. Farr
E. nemorosa × marshallii. Farr

119

E. confusa Pugsl. (107, 108)
Moorland and coastal pastures. Occasional.

CREICH	——	——	DORNOCH	GOLSPIE	CLYNE	——	——
ASSYNT	——		DURNESS	TONGUE	FARR		

E. brevipila Burnat & Gremli (107, 108)
Pastures, fields and roadsides. Common.

CREICH	LAIRG	ROGART	DORNOCH	GOLSPIE	CLYNE	LOTH	KILDONAN
ASSYNT	EDDRACHILLIS		DURNESS	TONGUE	FARR		

E. brevipila × micrantha. Assynt, Eddrachillis, Durness, Farr, Dornoch
E. brevipila × curta. Dornoch

var. reayensis Pugsl. (108)
Pastures. Occasional.

——	——	——	——	——
ASSYNT	EDDRACHILLIS	DURNESS	TONGUE	FARR

Assynt (Achmelvich)
Eddrachillis (Oldshoremore)
Tongue (Melness)
Farr (Bettyhill, Farr, Armadale & Port Skerra)

E. brevipila var. **reayensis × marshallii.** Assynt and Farr
E. brevipila var. **reayensis × micrantha.** Assynt
E. brevipila var. **reayensis × nemorosa.** Farr and Tongue

Odontites Ludw.

O. verna (Bellardi) Dumort sub sp. **verna** (107, 108) Red Bartsia
Cultivated fields and roadsides in coastal areas. Frequent.

CREICH	LAIRG	——	DORNOCH	GOLSPIE	CLYNE	LOTH	KILDONAN
ASSYNT	EDDRACHILLIS		DURNESS	TONGUE	FARR		

OROBANCHACEAE
Orobanche L

O. alba Steph. ex Willd. (108) Thyme Broomrape or Red Broomrape
On sea cliffs. Very rare.
Eddrachillis (Oldshoremore)

LENTIBULARIACEAE
Pinguicula L.

P. lusitanica L. (107, 108) Pale Butterwort
In bogs. Frequent in the west.

120

CREICH LAIRG —— —— —— —— —— KILDONAN
ASSYNT EDDRACHILLIS DURNESS TONGUE FARR

P. vulgaris L. (107, 108) Common Butterwort
Bogs, wet heaths. Common, widespread.
CREICH LAIRG ROGART DORNOCH GOLSPIE CLYNE LOTH KILDONAN
ASSYNT EDDRACHILLIS DURNESS TONGUE FARR

Ultricularia L.

U. neglecta Lehm. (108) Greater Bladderwort
In lochans. Rare.

—— —— —— —— —— ——

ASSYNT EDDRACHILLIS DURNESS —— ——
Assynt (Little Assynt, 1939, P.M.H., Stoer, 1944, A.J.W.)
Eddrachillis (Sandwood, 1952, M.McC.W.)
Durness (Farrmheal, 1960, D.A.R.)

U. intermedia Hayne (108) Intermediate Bladderwort
In lochs and lochans. Frequent in the north and west.

—— —— —— —— —— —— —— ——

ASSYNT EDDRACHILLIS DURNESS TONGUE FARR

U. minor L. (108) Lesser Bladderwort
In lochans. Rare.

—— —— —— —— ——

ASSYNT EDDRACHILLIS —— ——
Assynt (1833, R.G., Achumore, 1886, A.G.)
Eddrachillis (Scourie, 1939, P.M.H. & E.C.W.)

LABIATAE
Mentha L.

M. arvensis L. (107, 108) Corn Mint
In cultivated fields. Rare.
—— LAIRG —— —— —— —— —— KILDONAN
—— —— —— TONGUE FARR

M.×verticillata L. (108)
Near gardens. Local.
Tongue (Tongue)

M.×gentilis L. (108)
Sides of ditches. Local.
Assynt (Stoer, 1944, A.J.W.)

121

M. aquatica L. (107, 108) Water Mint
Ditches, marshes, streams and lakes. Frequent.
CREICH LAIRG ROGART DORNOCH GOLSPIE CLYNE LOTH KILDONAN
ASSYNT EDDRACHILLIS DURNESS TONGUE FARR

M. × **piperita** L. (108) Peppermint
var. **piperita**
Sides of ditches. Local.
Tongue (Tongue)
Farr (Bettyhill, Melvich)

M. spicata L. (107, 108) Spear Mint
Damp places. An escape.
―― ―― ROGART DORNOCH ―― CLYNE LOTH KILDONAN
ASSYNT EDDRACHILLIS DURNESS ―― FARR

M. × **cordifolia** Opiz (107)
Damp places. Local.
Kildonan (Helmsdale)

M. × **niliaca** Jussex Jacq. (107, 108)
Damp places. Local.
Clyne (Strath Brora, 1948, W.A.T.)
Assynt (Lochinver, 1944, A.J.W.)
Farr (Melvich)

Lycopus L.

L. europaeus L. (107, 108) Gipsywort
Damp places. Rare.
―― ―― ―― ―― ―― ―― LOTH KILDONAN
―― EDDRACHILLIS DURNESS ―― ――

Thymus L.

T. drucei Ronn. (107, 108) Wild Thyme
Dry grassland, dunes, heaths and screes. Common, widespread.
CREICH LAIRG ROGART DORNOCH GOLSPIE CLYNE LOTH KILDONAN
ASSYNT EDDRACHILLIS DURNESS TONGUE FARR

Acinos Mill

A. arvensis (Lam.) Dandy (107) Basil Thyme

122

On railway-bank. Casual.
Creich (Invershin, 1890, E.S.M. & F.J.H.)

Prunella L.

P. vulgaris L. (107, 108) Selfheal
Grassy places. Common, widespread.
CREICH LAIRG ROGART DORNOCH GOLSPIE CLYNE LOTH KILDONAN
ASSYNT EDDRACHILLIS DURNESS TONGUE FARR

Stachys L.

S. arvensis (L.) L. (107, 108) Field Woundwort
In cultivated fields. Rare.
—— —— —— —— —— —— —— KILDONAN
—— EDDRACHILLIS DURNESS TONGUE FARR
Kildonan (Helmsdale, 1889, W.R.L.)
Eddrachillis (Kinlochbervie, 1952, M.McC.W.)
Durness (Durness, 1887, E.S.M.)
Tongue (Tongue, 1833, H.C.W.)
Farr (Bettyhill, 1890, W.F.M.)

S. palustris L. (107, 108) Marsh Woundwort
Ditches, marshes. Frequent.
CREICH LAIRG ROGART DORNOCH GOLSPIE CLYNE LOTH KILDONAN
ASSYNT EDDRACHILLIS DURNESS TONGUE FARR

S. sylvatica L. (107, 108) Hedge Woundwort
Woods and damp shady places. Frequent.
CREICH LAIRG ROGART DORNOCH GOLSPIE CLYNE LOTH KILDONAN
ASSYNT EDDRACHILLIS DURNESS TONGUE FARR

S. × ambigua Sm. (S. palustris × sylvatica) (107, 108)
Ditches. Occasional.
—— LAIRG —— DORNOCH —— —— —— ——
ASSYNT EDDRACHILLIS DURNESS TONGUE FARR

Lamium L.

L. amplexicaule L. (107, 108) Henbit Dead-nettle
Cultivated fields. Occasional.
CREICH LAIRG —— DORNOCH GOLSPIE CLYNE LOTH KILDONAN
ASSYNT EDDRACHILLIS DURNESS TONGUE FARR

L. molucellifolium Fr. (107, 108) Northern Dead-nettle

123

Cultivated fields. Occasional.

—— LAIRG —— —— —— CLYNE LOTH KILDONAN
ASSYNT EDDRACHILLIS DURNESS TONGUE FARR

L. hybridum Vill. (108) Cut-leaved Dead-nettle
In cultivated field. Rare.

—— —— —— —— —— —— —— ——
—— —— —— —— —— FARR

L. purpureum L. (107, 108) Red Dead-nettle
Cultivated fields and waste places. Frequent.
CREICH LAIRG ROGART DORNOCH GOLSPIE CLYNE LOTH KILDONAN
ASSYNT EDDRACHILLIS DURNESS TONGUE FARR

L. album L. (108) White Dead-nettle
Waste places. Casual.

—— EDDRACHILLIS DURNESS TONGUE ——
Eddrachillis (Kinlochbervie, 1952, M.McC.W.)
Durness (Durness)
Tongue (Tongue, 1845, H.M.McK., 1888, A.G.)

Galeopsis L.

G. tetrahit L. (107, 108) Common Hemp-nettle
Fields and waste places. Common.
CREICH LAIRG ROGART DORNOCH GOLSPIE CLYNE LOTH KILDONAN
ASSYNT EDDRACHILLIS DORNOCH TONGUE FARR

G. bifida Boenn. (107, 108) Hemp-nettle
Fields and waste places. Occasional.
CREICH —— —— —— —— —— ——
—— —— DURNESS —— FARR

G. speciosa Mill. (108) Large-flowered Hemp-nettle
Fields and waste places. Rare.

—— EDDRACHILLIS DURNESS —— ——

Glechoma L.

G. hederacea L. (107, 108) Ground Ivy
Woods. Occasional.
CREICH —— ROGART —— GOLSPIE CLYNE —— ——
—— —— DURNESS —— ——

Scutellaria L.

S. galericulata L. (107, 108) Skullcap
Wet grassy places. Occasional.
CREICH ——— ROGART ——— ——— ——— ——— ———
ASSYNT EDDRACHILLIS DURNESS TONGUE ———

Teucrium L.

T. scorodonia L. (107, 108) Wood Sage
Woods, dry heaths, dunes and screes. Common.
CREICH LAIRG ROGART DORNOCH GOLSPIE CLYNE LOTH KILDONAN
ASSYNT EDDRACHILLIS DURNESS TONGUE FARR

Ajuga L.

A. reptans L. (107, 108) Bugle
Damp woods and banks. Ascends to 1400 ft on Ben Griam. Occasional.
CREICH LAIRG ROGART DORNOCH GOLSPIE CLYNE ——— KILDONAN
ASSYNT EDDRACHILLIS DURNESS ——— FARR

A. pyramidalis L. (107, 108) Pyramidal Bugle
Ledges on basic rocks. Occasional.
CREICH ——— ——— DORNOCH GOLSPIE ——— LOTH KILDONAN
ASSYNT EDDRACHILLIS DURNESS ——— FARR

PLANTAGINACEAE
Plantago L.

P. major L. (107, 108) Greater Plantain
Fields, roadsides and waste places. Common, widespread.
CREICH LAIRG ROGART DORNOCH GOLSPIE CLYNE LOTH KILDONAN
ASSYNT EDDRACHILLIS DURNESS TONGUE FARR

P. lanceolata L. (107, 108) Ribwort Plantain
Grassy places, dunes, roadsides and waste places. Common, widespread.
CREICH LAIRG ROGART DORNOCH GOLSPIE CLYNE LOTH KILDONAN
ASSYNT EDDRACHILLIS DURNESS TONGUE FARR

P. maritima L. (107, 108) Sea Plantain
Salt marshes, sea-cliffs, dunes, rocks and pastures on mountains.
Common, widespread.
CREICH LAIRG ROGART DORNOCH GOLSPIE CLYNE LOTH KILDONAN
ASSYNT EDDRACHILLIS DURNESS TONGUE FARR

P. coronopus L. (107, 108) Buck's-horn Plantain
Sandy and stony places and cliffs by the sea. Frequent.

			DORNOCH	GOLSPIE	CLYNE		KILDONAN
ASSYNT	EDDRACHILLIS		DURNESS	TONGUE	FARR		

Littorella Berg.

L. uniflora (L.) Aschers. (107, 108) Shoreweed
Sandy and gravelly shores of lakes. Frequent.

CREICH	LAIRG			GOLSPIE	CLYNE		KILDONAN
ASSYNT	EDDRACHILLIS		DURNESS	TONGUE	FARR		

CAMPANULACEAE
Campanula L.

C. latifolia L. (107) Giant Bellflower
Woods. Rare.
Golspie (*Dunrobin*)

C. rapunculoides L. (107) Creeping Campunula or Creeping Bellflower
Near gardens. Escape.
Dornoch (*Ferrytown*)
Kildonan (*Kildonan*)

C. rotundifolia L. (107, 108) Bluebell or Harebell
Pastures, banks, dunes, heaths. Frequent.

CREICH	LAIRG	ROGART	DORNOCH	GOLSPIE	CLYNE	LOTH	KILDONAN
ASSYNT	EDDRACHILLIS		DURNESS	TONGUE	FARR		

Lobelia L.

L. dortmanna L. (107, 108) Water Lobelia
Gravelly margins of lakes. Common.

	LAIRG	ROGART			CLYNE		KILDONAN
ASSYNT	EDDRACHILLIS		DURNESS	TONGUE	FARR		

RUBIACEAE
Sherardia L.

S. arvensis L. (107, 108) Field Madder
Fields. Occasional.

CREICH		ROGART			CLYNE		KILDONAN
ASSYNT			DURNESS	TONGUE			

126

Galium L.

G. odoratum (L.) Scop. (107, 108) Woodruff
Woods and shady banks. Occasional.
—— —— ROGART DORNOCH —— —— —— KILDONAN
ASSYNT —— DURNESS TONGUE FARR

G. boreale L. (107, 108) Northern Bedstraw
Banks of streams. Frequent.
CREICH LAIRG ROGART DORNOCH GOLSPIE —— —— KILDONAN
ASSYNT EDDRACHILLIS DURNESS —— ——

G. mollugo L. sub sp. **mollugo** (107) Great Hedge Bedstraw
Roadsides. Introduced. Rare.
—— LAIRG ROGART DORNOCH —— —— —— KILDONAN
—— —— —— —— —— ——

sub sp. **erectum** Syme. (107) Erect Hedge Bedstraw
Golspie (Golspie, 1903, G.C.D.)

G. verum L. (107, 108) Lady's Bedstraw
Dry grassy places and dunes. Common.
CREICH LAIRG ROGART DORNOCH GOLSPIE CLYNE LOTH KILDONAN
ASSYNT EDDRACHILLIS DURNESS TONGUE FARR

G. saxatile L. (107, 108) Heath Bedstraw
Grassy places and heaths. Common, widespread.
CREICH LAIRG ROGART DORNOCH GOLSPIE CLYNE LOTH KILDONAN
ASSYNT EDDRACHILLIS DURNESS TONGUE FARR

G. sterneri Ehrend. (107, 108) Limestone Bedstraw or Slender Bedstraw
On calcareous grassland on hills. Occasional.
—— —— —— —— —— —— —— KILDONAN
ASSYNT EDDRACHILLIS DURNESS —— FARR

G. palustre L. (107, 108) Common Marsh-bedstraw
Marshes and ditches. Common, widespread.
CREICH LAIRG ROGART DORNOCH GOLSPIE CLYNE LOTH KILDONAN
ASSYNT EDDRACHILLIS DURNESS TONGUE FARR

G. aparine L. (107, 108) Cleavers or Goosegrass
Roadsides, waste places, shingle beaches. Common.
CREICH LAIRG ROGART DORNOCH GOLSPIE CLYNE LOTH KILDONAN
ASSYNT EDDRACHILLIS DURNESS TONGUE FARR

127

CAPRIFOLIACEAE
Sambucus L.

S. ebulus L. (107) Dwarf Elder or Danewort
At roadside. Introduced. Rare.
Golspie (Golspie, 1962, M.McC.W.)

S. nigra L. (107, 108) Elder
Amongst scrub, roadsides and waste places. Always near houses.
Very sparse in the north and west. Introduced.
CREICH LAIRG ROGART DORNOCH GOLSPIE CLYNE LOTH KILDONAN
ASSYNT EDDRACHILLIS DURNESS TONGUE FARR

Viburnum L.

V. opulus L. (107, 108) Guelder Rose
Amongst scrub. Rare.
CREICH —— —— —— —— —— —— ——
ASSYNT EDDRACHILLIS DURNESS —— ——
Creich (Rosehall)
Assynt (Inchnadamph)
Eddrachillis (Glendhu)
Durness (Koeldale)

Symphoricarpos Duham

S. rivularis Suksd. (107, 108) Snowberry
Garden escape.
Kildonan (Suisgill)
Tongue (Tongue)

Linnaea L.

L. borealis L. (107) Twinflower or Linnaea
In coniferous woods. Very rare.
—— —— —— —— GOLSPIE —— —— ——
Golspie (Golspie, 1888, J.G., 1960, J.A.)

Lonicera L.

L. periclymenum L. (107, 108) Honeysuckle
Woods, hedges. Common.
CREICH LAIRG ROGART DORNOCH GOLSPIE CLYNE LOTH KILDONAN
ASSYNT EDDRACHILLIS DURNESS TONGUE FARR

128

ADOXACEAE
Adoxa L.

A. moschatellina L. (108) Moschatel or Townhall Clock
Assynt (*Knockan, 1895, G.S.D.*) *No recent record.*

VALERIANACEAE
Valerianella Mill.

V. locusta (L.) Betcke (107, 108) Common Cornsalad or Lamb's Lettuce
Dunes and fields. Rare.

—— —— —— GOLSPIE —— —— ——
—— EDDRACHILLIS DURNESS —— ——
Golspie (*Strathsteven, 1888, J.G.*)

Valeriana L.

V. officinalis L. (107, 108) Common Valerian
Ditches and amongst scrub. Common.

CREICH LAIRG ROGART DORNOCH GOLSPIE CLYNE LOTH KILDONAN
ASSYNT EDDRACHILLIS DURNESS TONGUE FARR

DIPSACACEAE
Knautia L.

K. arvensis (L.) Coult. (108) Field Scabious
Fields and dunes. Occasional.

—— —— —— —— —— —— —— ——
—— —— DURNESS TONGUE FARR

Succisa Haller

S. pratensis Moench (107, 108) Devil's-bit Scabious
Damp pastures, heaths. Common, widespread.

CREICH LAIRG ROGART DORNOCH GOLSPIE CLYNE LOTH KILDONAN
ASSYNT EDDRACHILLIS DURNESS TONGUE FARR

COMPOSITAE
Senecio L.

S. jacobaea L. (107, 108) Common Ragwort
Pastures, dunes, waste places. Common, widespread.

CREICH LAIRG ROGART DORNOCH GOLSPIE CLYNE LOTH KILDONAN
ASSYNT EDDRACHILLIS DURNESS TONGUE FARR
var. **discoideus** Koch. On the north coast.

S. aquaticus Hill (107, 108) Marsh Ragwort
Marshes, ditches, banks of streams. Common.
CREICH LAIRG ROGART DORNOCH GOLSPIE CLYNE LOTH KILDONAN
ASSYNT EDDRACHILLIS DURNESS TONGUE FARR

S. sylvaticus L. (107, 108) Heath or Wood Groundsel
Open grassy places. Frequent in the east, sparse in north and west.
CREICH LAIRG ROGART DORNOCH GOLSPIE CLYNE LOTH KILDONAN
ASSYNT —— DURNESS —— FARR

S. viscosus L. (107) Sticky Groundsel or Stinking Groundsel
Waste places. Occasional.
—— —— —— DORNOCH GOLSPIE —— —— KILDONAN

S. vulgaris L. (107, 108) Groundsel
Waste ground, gardens, cultivated fields. Common.
CREICH LAIRG ROGART DORNOCH GOLSPIE CLYNE LOTH KILDONAN
ASSYNT EDDRACHILLIS DURNESS TONGUE FARR

Tussilago L.

T. farfara L. (107, 108) Colt's-foot
Waste places, screes, dunes, banks, shingle. Common.
CREICH LAIRG ROGART DORNOCH GOLSPIE CLYNE LOTH KILDONAN
ASSYNT EDDRACHILLIS DURNESS TONGUE FARR

Petasites Mill.

P. albus (L.) Gaertn. (107) White Butterbur
On roadside. Garden escape.
Dornoch (Dornoch)

Filago L.

F. germanica (L.) L. (107) Common Cudweed
Dry heaths. Very rare.
—— —— —— —— —— CLYNE —— ——
—— —— —— —— —— ——

Clyne (Brora)

F. minima (Sm.) Pers. (107) Slender Cudweed or Small Cudweed
Sandy heaths and fields. Occasional.
CREICH LAIRG ROGART DORNOCH GOLSPIE CLYNE —— KILDONAN

130

Gnaphalium L.

G. sylvaticum L. (107, 108) Heath or Wood Cudweed
Heaths and woods. Frequent.

CREICH	LAIRG	ROGART	DORNOCH	GOLSPIE	CLYNE	LOTH	KILDONAN
ASSYNT	EDDRACHILLIS		DURNESS	TONGUE	FARR		

G. supinum L. (107, 108) Dwarf Cudweed
Bare places on mountain tops. Frequent.

CREICH	——	——	——	——	——	——	——
ASSYNT	EDDRACHILLIS		DURNESS	TONGUE	FARR		

G. uliginosum L. (107, 108) Marsh Cudweed
Damp fields and heaths. Occasional.

——	——	——	——	——	——	——	KILDONAN
ASSYNT	EDDRACHILLIS	——		TONGUE	FARR		

    Antennaria Gaertn.

A. dioica (L.) Gaertn. (107, 108) Mountain Everlasting or Cat's-foot
Dry pastures, heaths, dunes and on mountains. Common.

CREICH	LAIRG	ROGART	DORNOCH	GOLSPIE	CLYNE	LOTH	KILDONAN
ASSYNT	EDDRACHILLIS		DURNESS	TONGUE	FARR		

    Solidago L.

S. virgaurea L. (107, 108) Goldenrod
Dunes, pastures, banks and rocks. From sea-level to 3000 ft. Common.

CREICH	LAIRG	ROGART	DORNOCH	GOLSPIE	CLYNE	LOTH	KILDONAN
ASSYNT	EDDRACHILLIS		DURNESS	TONGUE	FARR		

    Aster L.

A. tripolium L. (107, 108) Sea Aster
Salt-marshes. Occasional.

CREICH	——	——	DORNOCH	GOLSPIE	——	——	KILDONAN
ASSYNT	EDDRACHILLIS		DURNESS	TONGUE	FARR		

    Bellis L.

B. perennis L. (107, 108) Daisy
Grasslands, roadsides. Common, widespread.

CREICH	LAIRG	ROGART	DORNOCH	GOLSPIE	CLYNE	LOTH	KILDONAN
ASSYNT	EDDRACHILLIS		DURNESS	TONGUE	FARR		

Eupatorium L.

E. cannabinum L. (108) Hemp-agrimony
Farr (Bettyhill, 1833, H.C.W.)

Anthemis L.

A. tinctoria L. (107) Yellow Chamomile
On railway bank. Casual.
Creich (Invershin, 1890, E.S.M. & F.J.H.)

Achillea L.

A. millefolium L. (107, 108) Yarrow
Fields, roadsides, dunes. Common, widespread.
CREICH LAIRG ROGART DORNOCH GOLSPIE CLYNE LOTH KILDONAN
ASSYNT EDDRACHILLIS DURNESS TONGUE FARR

A. ptarmica L. (107, 108) Sneezewort
Damp meadows, ditches. Common.
CREICH LAIRG ROGART DORNOCH GOLSPIE CLYNE LOTH KILDONAN
ASSYNT EDDRACHILLIS DURNESS TONGUE FARR

Tripleurospermum Schultz Bip.

T. maritimum (L.) Koch (107, 108) Scentless Mayweed
sub sp. **maritimum**
Dunes, shingle beaches and sea-cliffs. Frequent.
——— ——— ——— DORNOCH GOLSPIE CLYNE LOTH KILDONAN
ASSYNT EDDRACHILLIS DURNESS TONGUE FARR
sub sp. **inodorum** (L.) Hyland. ex Vaarama
Fields and waste places. Frequent.
CREICH LAIRG ROGART DORNOCH GOLSPIE CLYNE LOTH KILDONAN
——— ——— DURNESS TONGUE FARR

Matricaria L.

M. recutita L. (107) Scented Mayweed or Wild Chamomile
Railway bank. Casual.
Golspie (Golspie, 1888, J.G.)

M. matricarioides (Less.) Porter (107, 108) Pineapple weed or
Rayless Mayweed
Waysides, waste places, fields. Common.

132

CREICH   LAIRG   ROGART   DORNOCH   GOLSPIE   CLYNE   LOTH   KILDONAN
ASSYNT   EDDRACHILLIS   DURNESS   TONGUE   FARR

Chrysanthemum L.

C. segetum L. (107, 108) Corn Marigold
In cultivated fields. Frequent.
CREICH   LAIRG   ROGART   DORNOCH   GOLSPIE   CLYNE   LOTH   KILDONAN
ASSYNT   EDDRACHILLIS   DURNESS   TONGUE   FARR

C. leucanthemum L. (107, 108) Oxeye Daisy
Fields, waysides, dunes. Frequent.
CREICH   LAIRG   ROGART   DORNOCH   GOLSPIE   CLYNE   LOTH   KILDONAN
ASSYNT   EDDRACHILLIS   DURNESS   TONGUE   FARR

C. parthenium (L.) Bernh. (107, 108) Feverfew
Roadsides, walls. Occasional.
CREICH   LAIRG   ROGART   DORNOCH   GOLSPIE   CLYNE   LOTH   KILDONAN
ASSYNT   EDDRACHILLIS   DURNESS   TONGUE   FARR

C. vulgare (L.) Bernh. (107, 108) Tansy
Waste places, near gardens. Occasional.
CREICH   LAIRG   ROGART   DORNOCH   GOLSPIE   CLYNE   LOTH   KILDONAN
ASSYNT   EDDRACHILLIS   DURNESS   TONGUE   FARR

Artemisia L.

A. vulgaris L. (107, 108) Mugwort
Fields and waste places near the sea. Occasional.
————   ————   ————   DORNOCH   GOLSPIE   ————   ————   KILDONAN
ASSYNT   EDDRACHILLIS   DURNESS   TONGUE   FARR

A. absinthium L. (108) Wormwood
In old neglected garden.
Assynt (*Achmelvich*)

Arctium L.

A. minus Bernh. Lesser Burdock
sub sp. **nemorosum** (Lejeune) Syme (107, 108)
Waste places. Frequent.
CREICH   LAIRG   ROGART   DORNOCH   GOLSPIE   CLYNE   LOTH   KILDONAN
ASSYNT   EDDRACHILLIS   DURNESS   TONGUE   FARR

Carduus L.

C. tenuiflorus Curt. (107) Slender Thistle
Waste places near the sea. Occasional.

—— —— —— DORNOCH GOLSPIE —— —— KILDONAN
—— —— ——

C. nutans L. (108) Musk Thistle
Casual (one plant)
Assynt (Lochinver)

Cirsium Mill.

C. vulgare (Savi) Ten. (107, 108) Spear Thistle
Waste places, roadsides. Common, widespread.
CREICH LAIRG ROGART DORNOCH GOLSPIE CLYNE LOTH KILDONAN
ASSYNT EDDRACHILLIS DURNESS TONGUE FARR

C. palustre (L.) Scop. (107, 108) Marsh Thistle
Marshes, ditches, wet woods. Common, widespread.
CREICH LAIRG ROGART DORNOCH GOLSPIE CLYNE LOTH KILDONAN
ASSYNT EDDRACHILLIS DURNESS TONGUE FARR

C. arvense (L.) Scop. (107, 108) Creeping Thistle
Fields, waste places. Common.
CREICH LAIRG ROGART DORNOCH GOLSPIE CLYNE LOTH KILDONAN
ASSYNT EDDRACHILLIS DURNESS TONGUE FARR

C. heterophyllum (L.) Hill (107, 108) Melancholy Thistle
Wet places by streams, on banks and hills. Frequent.
CREICH —— ROGART —— —— CLYNE —— ——
ASSYNT EDDRACHILLIS DURNESS TONGUE FARR

Saussurea DC.

S. alpina (L.) DC. (107, 108) Alpine Saw-wort or Alpine Saussurea
Mountain rocks and cliffs. Descends to 400 ft. Occasional.
CREICH —— —— —— —— —— —— KILDONAN
ASSYNT EDDRACHILLIS DURNESS TONGUE FARR

Centaurea L.

C. scabiosa L. (108) Greater Knapweed
Fields and dunes. Occasional on north coast.

—— —— —— —— —— —— —— ——

—— EDDRACHILLIS DURNESS TONGUE FARR

C. cyanus L. (107, 108) Cornflower
Cornfields. Rare. Extinct in v.c. 108.

				GOLSPIE		LOTH	KILDONAN
ASSYNT					FARR		

Assynt (Inchnadamph, 1899, G.E.S.)
Farr (Bettyhill, 1888, W.C.)

C. nigra L. sub sp. **nigra** (107, 108) Common Knapweed or
Lesser Knapweed
Waysides, fields. Common.

CREICH	LAIRG	ROGART	DORNOCH	GOLSPIE	CLYNE	LOTH	KILDONAN
ASSYNT	EDDRACHILLIS		DURNESS	TONGUE	FARR		

Lapsana L.

L. communis L. (107, 108) Nipplewort
Waysides, waste places and fields. Frequent.

CREICH	LAIRG	ROGART	DORNOCH	GOLSPIE	CLYNE	LOTH	KILDONAN
ASSYNT	EDDRACHILLIS		DURNESS	TONGUE	FARR		

Hypochoeris L.

H. radicata L. (107, 108) Cat's-ear
Pastures, dunes, roadsides. Common, widespread.

CREICH	LAIRG	ROGART	DORNOCH	GOLSPIE	CLYNE	LOTH	KILDONAN
ASSYNT	EDDRACHILLIS		DURNESS	TONGUE	FARR		

Leontodon L.

L. autumnalis L. (107, 108) Autumn Hawkbit
Pastures, dunes, roadsides. Common, widespread.

CREICH	LAIRG	ROGART	DORNOCH	GOLSPIE	CLYNE	LOTH	KILDONAN
ASSYNT	EDDRACHILLIS		DURNESS	TONGUE	FARR		

var. **autumnalis**. Roadsides and walls mainly in the east.
var. **pratensis**. Pastures in the north and west.
var. **simplex**. Short coastal turf on the north coast.

L. hispidus L. (107) Rough Hawkbit
Pastures. Rare.

		ROGART					KILDONAN

Rogart (Rogart)
Kildonan (Helmsdale)

135

K

L. taraxacoides (Vill) Mérat (108) Hairy Hawkbit or Lesser Hawkbit
On sandy ground. Rare.
Eddrachillis (Sheigra, 1966, A.G.K.)

Tragopogon L.

T. pratensis L. sub sp. **minor** (Mill.) Wahlenb. (108) Goat's-beard
Dunes. Occasional.

—— EDDRACHILLIS —— TONGUE FARR

Mycelis Cass.

M. muralis (L.) Dumort. (107) Wall Lettuce
Roadside. Casual.
Dornoch (Dornoch, 1966, J.A.)

Sonchus L.

S. arvensis L. (107, 108) Field Milk-Thistle or Perennial Sow-thistle
Cultivated fields, wet sandy shores. Occasional.

CREICH			DORNOCH	GOLSPIE			KILDONAN
ASSYNT	EDDRACHILLIS	DURNESS	TONGUE	FARR			

S. oleraceus L. (107, 108) Smooth Sow-Thistle
Cultivated fields and waste places. Frequent.

CREICH	LAIRG	ROGART	DORNOCH	GOLSPIE	CLYNE	LOTH	KILDONAN
ASSYNT	EDDRACHILLIS	DURNESS	TONGUE	FARR			

S. asper (L.) Hill (107, 108) Prickly Sow-thistle
Cultivated fields, waste places. Frequent.

CREICH	LAIRG	ROGART	DORNOCH	GOLSPIE	CLYNE	LOTH	KILDONAN
ASSYNT	EDDRACHILLIS	DURNESS	TONGUE	FARR			

Hieracium L.

Sub-genus **Pilosella** (Hill.) S. F. Gray
Section **Pilosellina** Pugsl.

H. pilosella L. (107, 108) Mouse-ear Hawkweed
Grassy places, banks, walls, heaths. Common, widespread.

CREICH	LAIRG	ROGART	DORNOCH	GOLSPIE	CLYNE	LOTH	KILDONAN
ASSYNT	EDDRACHILLIS	DURNESS	TONGUE	FARR			

var. **concinnatum** F. J. Hanb. (108)

Assynt (Knockan, 1958, M.McC.W., Inchnadamph, 1959, C.W.,
Culkein–Drumbeg, 1964, A.G.K.)
Eddrachillis (Oldshoremore, 1964, A.G.K.)
Durness (Balnakeil, 1959, C.W.)
Farr (Farr Bay, 1959, C.W.)

var. **tricholepium** (Neag & Petes) Pugsl. (108)
Assynt (Inchnadamph, 1959, C.W., Culkein–Drumbeg, 1964, A.G.K.)

Sub-genus **Hieracium**
Section **Alpina** Fries

H. holosericeum Backh. (107, 108)
Grassy slopes and rock-ledges at an altitude of 2500 ft or more.
Creich (Ben More Assynt, 1827, R.G.)
Assynt (Inchnadamph, 1900, T.J.F., Glass Beinn, 1960, A.G.K.)
Durness (Ben Hope, 1888, J.C.M.)

H. eximium Backh. var. **tenellum** Backh. (Druce) (108)
On rocky ledges over 2000 ft.
Farr (Ben Klibreck, 1897, E.S.M.)

H. gracilentum Backh. (108)
On rocky ledges or grassy slopes usually over 2500 ft.
Assynt (Canisp, 1890, E.S.M.)
Eddrachillis (Craig Riabbach and An Grianan, 1964, A.G.K.)

H. globosiflorum Pugsl. var. **globosiflorum** Pugsl. (108)
On rocky ledges and grassy slopes usually over 2500 ft.
Assynt (Canisp, 1890, E.S.M.)
Durness (Ben Hope, 1900, E.S.M.)

H. marginatum P. D. Sell & C. West (108)
On rocky ledges usually over 2500 ft.
Tongue (Ben Loyal, 1897, E.S.M.)
Farr (Ben Klibreck, 1897, E.S.M.)

H. pseudocurvatum (Zahn) Pugsl. (108)
On rocky ledges or grassy slopes usually over 2500 ft.
Durness (Ben Hope, 1890, E.F.L.)
Tongue (Ben Loyal, 1897, E.S.M.)

Section **Subalpina** Pugsl.

H. lingulatum Backh. ex Hook e Arnott (108)

137

Rocky ledges and stream sides over 2500 ft.
Assynt (Hills round Inchnadamph, 1908, E.S.M., 1957, R.C.P.)
Durness (Ben Hope, 1888, F.J.H., Foinaven and Carnstackie, 1964,
A.G.K.)
Tongue (Ben Loyal, 1897, E.S.M., 1953, C.W.)

H. hyparcticoides Pugsl. (108)
Rocky banks by streams.
Assynt (Hills and streams round Inchnadamph, 1890 & 1908, E.S.M.,
1957, C.W.)

H. callistophyllum F. J. Hanb. (107)
On stream sides and rocky ledges.
Creich (Oykell Bridge and Lubcroy, 1908, E.S.M.)

Section **Cerinthoidea** Fries

H. anglicum Fries (107, 108)
Rocky ledges, grassy banks and stream sides.
Dornoch (Cambusmore, 1962, M.McC.W.)
Assynt (Knockan, Inchnadamph, 1908, E.S.M.)
Durness (Koeldale, Ben Hope, 1953, M.C.F.P. & K.M.G.)
Tongue (Ben Loyal)
Farr (Farr Bay, 1951, C.W.)

H. hebridense Pugsl. (108)
Rocky streams, grassy banks and cliff-ledges.
Assynt (Inchnadamph, 1899, C.E.S., 1908, E.S.M., 1950, C.W.)
Durness (Ben Hope, H.W.P.)

H. ampliatum (W. R. Linton) A. Ley (108)
Cliff-ledges and rocky streams.
Assynt (Lochinver, 1890, E.S.M., Inchnadamph, 1908, E.S.M.)
Eddrachillis (Craig Riabbach, 1964, A.G.K.)
Durness (Ben Hope, Loch Eriboll, 1964, A.G.K.)
Tongue (Tongue Bay, 1897, E.S.M.)
Farr (Ben Klibreck, 1897, E.S.M.)

H. langwellense F. J. Hanb. (107, 108)
Rocky banks of streams.
Creich (Streams round Oykell Bridge, 1908, E.S.M., 1953, C.W.)
Lairg (Lairg, H.W.P.)
Kildonan (Torrish, 1957, M.McC.W., Helmsdale, 1888, E.F.L.)
Assynt (Streams round Inchnadamph, 1908, E.S.M.)
Durness (Ben Hope)

H. shoolbredii E. S. Marshall (108)
Rock-ledges and rocky banks of streams.
Assynt (Knockan, 1923, R.H.W., Elphin, Inchnadamph, 1899, C.E.S., 1908, E.S.M., 1950, C.W., 1956, R.A.G., Kylesku, 1890, F.J.H.)
Eddrachillis (Sandwood, 1957, M.McC.W., Craig Riabbach, 1964, A.G.K.)
Durness (Kearvaig & Koeldale, 1964, A.G.K., Durness, 1951, C.W., Smoo, 1923, R.H.W., 1951, C.W., Foinaven, 1964, C.W., Ben Hope, 1953, M.C.F.P.)
Tongue (Ben Loyal, 1897, E.S.M. & W.A.S., 1953, C.W.)
Farr (Invernaver, 1886, E.S.M., Bettyhill, 1888, E.F.L., 1955, M.McC.W., Farr Bay, 1915, E.S.M., 1951, C.W.)

H. iricum Fries (107, 108)
Rock-ledges, rocky banks of streams and grassy slopes.
Creich (Oykell Bridge, 1953, C.W.)
Assynt (Knockan, Lochinver, Skiag Bridge, Stoer, Inchnadamph, 1956, R.A.G. & R.M.H.)
Durness (Durness, 1856, D.O., 1887, E.S.M., Balnakeil)
Tongue (Coldbackie)
Farr (Invernaver, 1891, E.S.M., Farr Bay, 1953, M.McC.W., Melvich, 1952, C.W. & J.W.C.)

Section **Oreadea** Zahn.

H. schmidtii Tausch (108)
Eddrachillis (Sandwood, 1960, A.G.K.)
Farr (Invernaver, 1886, E.S.M., Bettyhill, 1888, E.F.L., Farr Bay, 1952, C.W., Melvich, 1952, C.W.)

H. nitidum Backh. (107, 108)
Rocky ledges.
Kildonan (Ben Griam, 1900, E.S.M.)
Assynt (Unapool, 1908, E.S.M., Inchnadamph, 1908, E.S.M., Culkein–Drumbeg, 1964, A.G.K.)
Eddrachillis (Badcall, 1885, F.J.H., Oldshoremore & Rhiconich, 1964, A.G.K.)
Durness (Ben Hope, 1900, E.S.M., 1888, F.J.H., Fashven, 1964, A.G.K.)
Tongue (Tongue, 1901, E.S.M).
Farr (Invernaver, 1897, E.S.M. & W.A.S., Farr Bay, 1915, E.S.M., 1915, C.W., Melvich, 1897, E.S.M.)

H. argenteum Fries (107, 108)
Rocky ledges, stream sides, grassy slopes and sand dunes.
Creich (Oykell Bridge, 1908, E.S.M.)
Golspie (Strathsteven, 1888, J.G., Golspie)

Clyne (Brora, 1897, E.S.M.)
Assynt (Knockan, 1894, G.C.D., Inchnadamph, 1897, E.S.M., Quinag, 1962, A.G.K.)
Eddrachillis (Sandwood, 1962, A.G.K.)
Durness (Ben Hope, 1888, F.J.H., Loch Hope, 1900, E.S.M., Durness, 1946, C.W.M.)
Tongue (Talmine, 1897, E.S.M., Tongue, 1897, E.S.M., Scullomie, 1900, E.S.M., Coldbackie, 1897, E.S.M., Skerray, 1900, E.S.M.)
Farr (Altnaharra, 1888 & 1915, E.S.M., Bettyhill, 1888, W.R.L., 1899, E.S.M., Farr Bay, 1951, C.W., Armadale, 1915, E.S.M., Kirtomy, Melvich, 1951, C.W., Strathy, 1956, J.A.)

H. scoticum F. J. Hanb. (108)
Rocky ledges and grassy banks.
Assynt (Inchnadamph, 1908, W.A.S.)
Tongue (Skerray, 1900, W.A.S.)
Farr (Farr Bay, 1897, W.R.L., 1951, C.W., Kirtomy, 1897, E.S.M., Armadale, 1888, W.R.L., Strathy, 1888, J.C.M., 1915, E.S.M., Melvich, 1915, F.J.H., 1951, C.W.)

Section **Suboreadea** Pugsl.

H. jovimontis (Zahn) Roffey (108)
Rocky ledges and banks.
Eddrachillis (Oldshoremore, 1964, A.G.K.)
Durness (Heilam Ferry, F.J.H.)
Farr (Altnaharra & Bettyhill, T.J.F.)

H. saxorum (F. J. Hanb.) Sell & West (107, 108)
Rocky ledges and stream sides.
Dornoch (Mound, 1962, M.McC.W.)
Tongue (Kinloch, 1897, E.S.M.)

H. dicella Sell & West (107, 108)
Limestone rocks.
Dornoch (Cambusmore, 1962, M.McC.W.)
Assynt (Inchnadamph, 1956, R.A.G. & R.M.H.)
Durness (Durness, 1956, J.A., Smoo, 1951, C.W.)

H. sarcophylloides Dahlst. (108)
Limestone cliffs.
Durness (Smoo, 1900, E.S.M., Seamraig, 1964, A.G.K.)
Farr (Altnaharra, 1888, J.C.)

Section **Vulgata** F. N. Williams

140

H. prolixum Noorlin (108)
Rocky ledges and sandhills.
Durness (Ben Hope, 1900, E.S.M.)
Tongue (Achininver, 1897, E.S.M.)

H. subtenue (W. R. Linton) Roffey (107, 108)
Rocky ledges and stream sides.
Creich (Streams round Oykell Bridge, 1908, W.A.S.)
Eddrachillis (Craig Riabbach, 1964, A.G.K.)
Assynt (Stoer, 1956, R.A.G., Canisp, 1899, C.E.S., Inchnadamph, 1908,
E.S.M.)
Durness (Ben Hope, 1900, E.S.M., Fashven, 1964, A.G.K.)
Tongue (Ben Loyal, 1900, E.S.M.)

H. aggregatum Backh. (108)
Rocky ledges.
Tongue (Skerray, E.S.M.) fide Pugsl.

H. camptopetalum (F. J. Hanb.) Sell & West (108)
Rocky stream sides and cliffs.
Assynt (Kylesku, 1908, E.S.M., Inchnadamph, 1908, E.S.M., 1951, C.W.)
Durness (Streams by Ben Hope, 1888, J.C.M., 1952, C.W.)

H. duriceps F. J. Hanb. (107, 108)
Rocky cliffs, stream sides and grassy banks.
Creich (Oykell Bridge, 1952, C.W.)
Assynt (Inchnadamph, 1890, E.S.M.)
Farr (Altnaharra, 1888, F.J.H., Ben Klibreck, 1897, E.S.M., Bettyhill
& Farr Bay, 1910, E.S.M.)

H. pollinarium F. J. Hanb. (108)
Rocky ledges.
Farr (Strathnaver, 1888, J.C.M., Invernaver, 1886, F.J.H., Farr Bay,
1915, E.S.M.)

H. pictorum E. F. Linton (107, 108)
Rocky cliffs and stream sides.
Creich (Oykell Bridge, 1908, E.S.M.)
Tongue (Ben Loyal, 1900, E.S.M.)

H. pollinarioides Pugsl. (108)
Limestone rocks.
Assynt (Inverkirkaig, 1944, A.J.W., Lochinver, 1890, E.S.M., 1944,
A.J.W., Stoer, 1956, R.A.G., Clashnessie, 1956, R.A.G.)
Eddrachillis (Oldshoremore, 1964, A.G.K.)

Durness (Smoo, 1923, R.H.W., 1958, U.K.D., Balnakeil, 1959, C.W.,
Durness, 1900, E.S.M.)
Farr (Bettyhill, 1953, M.McC.W.)

H. variicolor var. **piligerum** Pugsl. (108)
Rocky cliffs and stream sides.
Assynt (Culag, 1956, R.A.G., Inchnadamph, E.S.M.)
Durness (Ben Hope, 1900, E.S.M.)

H. dipteroides Dahlst. (108)
Rocky cliffs and stream sides.
Assynt (Beinn Garbh, 1908, W.A.S.)

H. rivale F. J. Hanb. (107, 108)
Rocky cliffs and stream sides.
Kildonan (Ben Griam Mor, 1963, M.McC.W.)
Assynt (Inchnadamph, 1890, F.J.H., 1908, E.S.M.)
Eddrachillis (Craig Riabbach, 1964, A.G.K.)
Durness (Carnstackie & Beinn Spionnaidh, 1964, A.G.K.)

H. euprepes F. J. Hanb. (108)
Rocky places, sand dunes and grassy banks.
Assynt (Stoer, 1956, R.A.G.)
Eddrachillis (Cnoc na Glaic Torsain, 1964, A.G.K.)
Durness (Balnakeil, 1953, M.C.F.P., Carnstackie & Farrmheal, 1964,
A.G.K.)
Tongue (Tongue Ferry, 1897, E.S.M. & W.A.S., 1900, E.S.M.)
Farr (Invernaver, 1888, W.R.L., Armadale, 1915, E.S.M., Melvich,
1897, E.S.M., Bettyhill, 1897, W.A.S.)

H. vennicontium Pugsl. (108)
Rocky stream sides.
Assynt (Ben Garbh, 1908, E.S.M.)

H. caesiomurorum Lindeb. (108)
Grassy banks and rocky stream sides.
Creich (1908, E.S.M.)
Assynt (Clachtoll, 1952, D.McC., Inchnadamph, 1900, C.E.S.)
Durness (Smoo, 1964, A.G.K.)
Tongue (Tongue & Ben Loyal, 1900, E.S.M.)
Farr (Forsinard, 1964, A.G.K.)

H. rubiginosum F. J. Hanb. (108)
Rocky stream sides.
Eddrachillis (Craig Ribbach & Rhiconich, 1962, A.G.K.)

H. cravoniense (F. J. Hanb.) Roffey (107, 108)
Grassy and rocky places.
Creich (*Oykell Bridge, F.J.H.*)
Dornoch (*Torboll, 1955, J.A.*)
Tongue (*Ardskinid, 1900, E.S.M.*)
Farr (*Farr Bay, 1951, C.W.*)

H. fulvocaesium Pugsl. (108)
Grassy banks.
Farr (*Bettyhill, 1887, E.S.M., 1953, J.E.R.*)

H. proximium F. J. Hanb. (108)
Sandhills.
Tongue (*Melness, 1897, E.S.M. & W.A.S.*)

H. caledonicum F. J. Hanb. (108)
On rocky ledges and stream sides.
Assynt (*Lochinver & Canisp, 1890, E.S.M., Inchnadamph, 1887, E.S.M.,
1908, E.S.M. & W.A.S., 1951, C.W.*)
Durness (*Balnakeil, 1948, M.McC.W., Fashven, Inshore, Kearvaig,
1964, A.G.K.*)
Tongue (*Ben Loyal, Melness, Tongue, 1897, E.S.M., Coldbackie, 1900,
E.S.M.*)
Farr (*Altnaharra, 1888, F.J.H., Strathnaver, 1888, J.C.M., Bettyhill,
Kirtomy, Melvich, 1897, E.S.M., Farr Bay, 1915, E.S.M., Strathy, 1915,
E.S.M.*)

H. vulgatum Fries (107, 108)
On rocks, grassy places, walls and dunes.
Creich (*Oykell Bridge, 1952, C.W. & J.W.C.*)
Golspie (*Golspie, 1950, C.W.*)
Clyne (*Brora, 1950, C.W. & J.W.C.*)
Kildonan (*Ord, 1960, J.A.*)
Assynt (*Inchnadamph & Kylesku, 1908, E.S.M., Knockan, 1958,
M.McC.W., Lochinver, Stoer & Clashnessie, 1956, R.A.G. & R.M.H.,
Loch Assynt, 1953, P.F.Y., Achmelvich, 1955, J.A., 1943, A.J.W.*)
Tongue (*Melness, 1897, E.S.M.*)
Farr (*Bettyhill, 1886, E.S.M., 1953, C.W. & J.W.C.*)

H. angustisquamum (Pugsl.) Pugsl. (108)
On limestone.
Assynt (*Ledmore, 1964, A.G.K.*)

Section **Alpestria** Fries

143

H. dovrense Fries (108)
Rocky ledges.
Eddrachillis (Rhiconich, 1964, A.G.K.)
Tongue (Ben Loyal, 1897, E.S.M., 1953, J.E.R.)

Section **Tridentata** Fries

H. sparsifolium Lindeb. (107, 108)
Grassy banks and rocky places.
Creich (Oykell Bridge, 1890, E.S.M., 1956, C.W.)
Assynt (Inchnadamph, 1923, R.H.W.)
Eddrachillis (Laxford Bridge)
Durness (Kearvaig, 1964, A.G.K.)
Tongue (Tongue, 1953, M.McC.W.)

Section **Foliosa** Pugsl.

H. latobrigorum (Zahn) Roffey (107, 108)
Grassy banks and rocks.
Creich (Bonar Bridge, H.W.P., Oykell Bridge, 1953, C.W.)
Clyne (Strath Brora, 1897, W.A.S.)
Durness (Koeldale, 1964, A.G.K.)
Tongue (Tongue, H.W.P.)
Farr (Altnaharra, 1887, E.S.M., Strathnaver, 1957, J.A., Bettyhill, 1952,
C.W., Farr, 1856, D.O., Armadale, Strathy, 1953, C.W., Melvich,
1953, C.W.)

H. subcrocatum (E. F. Linton) Roffey (107, 108)
Grassy places and banks of streams.
Clyne (Brora, 1957, M.McC.W.)
Assynt (Inverkirkaig, Achmelvich, 1944, A.J.W. & M.S.C.)
Farr (Bettyhill, 1954, J.E.R.)

H. strictiforme (Zahn) Roffey (108)
Grassy places and banks of streams.
Assynt (Inverkirkaig, 1944, A.J.W. & M.S.C., Inchnadamph, 1953, C.W.)
Durness (Inshore, Geodha Sligeach, 1964, A.G.K.)
Tongue (Melness, Tongue, Coldbackie, 1897, E.S.M.)
Farr (Altnaharra, 1889, W.F.M., 1897, E.S.M.)

H. reticulatum Lindeb. (107, 108)
Rocky banks of streams and grassy places.
Creich (Oykell Bridge, 1953, C.W.)
Tongue (Tongue, 1897, E.S.M., Skerray, 1959, C.W.)
Farr (Altnaharra, 1887, E.S.M., Bettyhill, 1951, C.W., Strathy, 1915,
E.S.M., 1951, C.W.)

H. maritimum (F. J. Hanb.) F. J. Hanb. (108)
Grassy banks and sandy places.
Tongue (*Skerray, 1900, E.S.M.*)
Farr (*Melvich, 1887, E.S.M., 1951, C.W.*)

Section **Umbellata** F. N. Williams

H. umbellatum L. (108)
sub sp. **umbellatum**
Grassy and sandy places.
Farr (*Farr Bay, 1827, R.G.*)

Crepis L.

C. capillaris (L.) Wallr. (107, 108) Smooth Hawk's-beard
Pastures, dunes, waste places. Common.

CREICH	LAIRG	ROGART	DORNOCH	GOLSPIE	CLYNE	LOTH	KILDONAN
ASSYNT	EDDRACHILLIS		DURNESS	TONGUE	FARR		

C. paludosa (L.) Moench (107, 108) Marsh Hawk's-beard
Wet grassy places. Frequent.

CREICH	LAIRG	ROGART	DORNOCH	GOLSPIE	CLYNE	LOTH	KILDONAN
ASSYNT	EDDRACHILLIS		DURNESS	TONGUE	FARR		

Taraxacum Weber

T. officinale Weber. (107, 108) Common Dandelion
Fields, waste places. Common, widespread.

CREICH	LAIRG	ROGART	DORNOCH	GOLSPIE	CLYNE	LOTH	KILDONAN
ASSYNT	EDDRACHILLIS		DURNESS	TONGUE	FARR		

T. palustre (Lyons) DC. (107, 108) Narrow-leaved Marsh Dandelion
Marshes. Frequent.

CREICH	LAIRG	——	DORNOCH	GOLSPIE	CLYNE	LOTH	KILDONAN
——	——		——	TONGUE	FARR		

T. spectabile Dahlst. (107, 108) Broad-leaved Marsh Dandelion
Bogs. Frequent.

——	——	——	——	——	——	——	KILDONAN
ASSYNT	EDDRACHILLIS		DURNESS	TONGUE	FARR		

T. laevigatum (Willd.) DC. (107, 108) Lesser Dandelion
Heaths and sandy ground. Frequent.

——	——	——	DORNOCH	GOLSPIE	CLYNE	——	——
ASSYNT	EDDRACHILLIS		DURNESS	TONGUE	FARR		

145

MONOCOTYLEDONES
JUNCAGINACEAE
Triglochin L.

T. palustris L. (107, 108) Marsh Arrowgrass
Marshes and wet meadows. Common.

CREICH LAIRG ROGART DORNOCH GOLSPIE   CLYNE LOTH   KILDONAN
ASSYNT EDDRACHILLIS   DURNESS TONGUE   FARR

T. maritima L. (107, 108) Sea Arrowgrass
Salt marshes. Frequent.

———— ———— ———— DORNOCH GOLSPIE ———— ———— KILDONAN
ASSYNT EDDRACHILLIS   DURNESS TONGUE   FARR

ZOSTERACEAE
Zostera L.

Z. marina L. (107, 108) Eelgrass
In the sea near low water. Very rare.

———— ———— ———— ———— GOLSPIE ———— ———— ————
ASSYNT ————

Golspie (Loch Fleet, 1888, J.G.)
Assynt (Oldany, 1955, B.F.)

Z. angustifolia (Hornem.) Reichb. (107, 108) Narrow-leaved Eelgrass
Muddy estuaries. Very rare.

———— ———— ———— ———— GOLSPIE ———— ———— ————
———— ———— ———— ———— TONGUE FARR

Golspie (Loch Fleet, 1897, E.S.M., 1888, J.G.)
Tongue (Kyle of Tongue, 1900, E.S.M.)

Z. noltii Hornem. (107) Dwarf Eelgrass
Muddy estuaries. Very rare.

———— ———— ———— ———— GOLSPIE ———— ———— ————
———— ———— ———— ————

Golspie (Loch Fleet, 1897, E.S.M. & W.A.S.)

POTAMOGETONACEAE
Potamogeton L.

P. natans L. (107, 108) Broad-leaved Pondweed
Lochs and lochans. Frequent.

CREICH LAIRG ROGART DORNOCH GOLSPIE   CLYNE LOTH   KILDONAN
ASSYNT EDDRACHILLIS   DURNESS TONGUE   FARR

P. polygonifolius Pourr. (107, 108) Bog Pondweed
Peaty pools in bogs and moors. Common, widespread.
CREICH LAIRG ROGART DORNOCH GOLSPIE CLYNE LOTH KILDONAN
ASSYNT EDDRACHILLIS DURNESS TONGUE FARR

P. lucens L. (108) Shining Pondweed
Assynt (Recorded by A. Gray, 1886)

P. gramineus L. (108) Various-leaved Pondweed
Lochs and lochans. Occasional.

ASSYNT EDDRACHILLIS DURNESS TONGUE FARR
*Assynt (Loch Awe, 1886, A.G., 1890, E.S.M., Stoer, 1944, A.J.W. &
M.S.C.)*
Durness (Durness, 1881, W.F.M.)
Tongue (Lochs Modsarie, Craisg, Hakel & Dubh, 1948, G.T.)
Farr (Loch Naver, 1888, F.J.H. & J.C.M.)

P. × nitens Weber (108)
Lochs and lochans. Rare.

ASSYNT EDDRACHILLIS —— TONGUE ——
Assynt (Lochinver, 1886, A.G., Loch an Aigeil, 1944, A.J.W. & M.S.C.)
Eddrachillis (Scourie, 1885, H.E.F. & F.J.H.)
Tongue (Loch Modsarie, 1948, G.T.)

P. alpinus Balb. (108) Red Pondweed
Lochans. Rare.

ASSYNT —— —— TONGUE ——
Assynt (Loch an Aigeal, 1948, A.J.W. & M.S.C.)
Tongue (Loch Slaim, 1948, G.T.)

P. praelongus Wulf. (108) Long-stalked Pondweed
In lochs. Rare.
CREICH —— —— —— —— ——
ASSYNT —— DURNESS ——
Creich (Loch Sail, 1969, U.K.D.)
Assynt (Loch Maol a Choire, 1936, J.E.L., Gillaroo Loch, 1890, E.S.M.)
Durness (Loch Borralie, 1948, G.T.)

P. perfoliatus L. (107, 108) Perfoliate Pondweed
In lochs. Occasional.

CREICH ——— ———   ———   ———   ———   ———
ASSYNT EDDRACHILLIS   DURNESS TONGUE   ———
Creich (Bonar Bridge, 1842, J.S., Loch Sail, 1969, U.K.D.)
Assynt (Loch Awe, 1886, A.G., 1890, F.J.H. & E.S.M., Loch Borralan,
1886, A.G., Loch an Ordain & Loch Bad na Muirichinn, 1944, A.J.W.
& M.S.C.)
Durness (Loch Croispol & Borralie, 1948, G.T., 1881, W.F.M.)
Tongue (Lochs Modsarie & Craisg, 1948, G.T.)

P. × cognatus Aschers. & Graebn. (108)
Lochs. Very rare.

———   ———   ———   DURNESS ———   ———
Durness (Loch Borralie, 1948, G.T.)

P. berchtoldii Fieb. (108) Small Pondweed
In lochs. Rare.

ASSYNT ———   ———   ———   ———
Assynt (Loch an Aigeil, 1944, A.J.W. & M.S.C.)

P. crispus L. (108) Curled Pondweed
Lochs. Rare.

——— EDDRACHILLIS ———   ———   ———
Eddrachillis (Sandwood)

P. filiformis Pers. (108) Slender-leaved Pondweed
In lochs. Rare.

ASSYNT ———   DURNESS ———   ———
Assynt (Loch Urigill, 1886, W.F.M., Loch an Aigeil, 1944, A.J.W. &
M.S.C.)
Durness (Loch Caladail, 1885, H.E.F. & F.J.H., Loch Borralie, 1948,
G.T.)

P. pectinatus L. (108) Fennel Pondweed
In lochs. Rare.

———   ———   ———   DURNESS ———   ———
Durness (Loch Borralie, 1948, G.T.)

RUPPIACEAE
Ruppia L.

R. maritima L. (107) Beaked Tasselweed or Tassel Pondweed
In salt-marsh. Very rare.
—— —— —— —— GOLSPIE —— —— ——
—— —— —— —— —— ——
Golspie (Little Ferry, 1962, M.McC.W.)

LILIACEAE
Tofieldia Huds.

T. pusilla (Michx.) Pers. (108) Scottish Asphodel
Marshes and by springs on hills. Rare.
ASSYNT —— DURNESS —— ——
Assynt (Inchnadamph)
Durness (Durness, Ben Hope)

Narthecium Huds.

N. ossifragum (L.) Huds. (107, 108) Bog Asphodel
Bogs and wet heaths. Common, widespread.
CREICH LAIRG ROGART DORNOCH GOLSPIE CLYNE LOTH KILDONAN
ASSYNT EDDRACHILLIS DURNESS TONGUE FARR

Ornithogalum L.

O. umbellatum L. (107) Star-of-Bethlehem
Introduced.
Clyne (Brora)

Scilla L.

S. verna Huds. (108) Spring Squill
Grassy turf near the sea. Occasional on the north coast.
—— EDDRACHILLIS DURNESS TONGUE FARR

Endymion Dumort.

E. non-scriptus (L.) Garcke (107, 108) Bluebell or Wild Hyacinth
In woods and amongst scrub. Frequent.
CREICH LAIRG ROGART DORNOCH GOLSPIE CLYNE LOTH KILDONAN
ASSYNT EDDRACHILLIS DURNESS TONGUE FARR

149

TRILLIACEAE
Paris L.

P. quadrifolia L. (108) Herb-Paris
Assynt (Islet in Loch Awe, 1895, G.C.D.)

JUNCACEAE
Juncus L.

J. squarrosus L. (107, 108) Heath Rush
Heaths and moors. Common, widespread.

CREICH LAIRG ROGART DORNOCH GOLSPIE CLYNE LOTH KILDONAN
ASSYNT EDDRACHILLIS DURNESS TONGUE FARR

J. tenuis Willd. (108) Slender Rush
Bare place by paths. Rare.

ASSYNT EDDRACHILLIS DURNESS ―― ――
Assynt (Lochinver)
Eddrachillis (Kylesku)
Durness (Durness)

J. gerardii Lois. (107, 108) Saltmarsh Rush or Mud Rush
Salt-marshes. Frequent.

CREICH ―― ―― DORNOCH GOLSPIE ―― ―― KILDONAN
ASSYNT EDDRACHILLIS DURNESS TONGUE FARR

J. trifidus L. (107, 108) Three-leaved Rush
Rock-ledges and stony places on many western hills. Ascends to 3000 ft.
Occasional.

CREICH ―― ―― ―― ―― ―― ――
ASSYNT EDDRACHILLIS DURNESS TONGUE FARR

J. bufonius L. (107, 108) Toad Rush
Roadsides, paths, muddy places. Common, widespread.

CREICH LAIRG ROGART DORNOCH GOLSPIE CLYNE LOTH KILDONAN
ASSYNT EDDRACHILLIS DURNESS TONGUE FARR

J. effusus L. (107, 108) Soft Rush
Wet pastures, bogs. Common, widespread.

CREICH LAIRG ROGART DORNOCH GOLSPIE CLYNE LOTH KILDONAN
ASSYNT EDDRACHILLIS DURNESS TONGUE FARR

J. conglomeratus L. (107, 108) Compact Rush
Wet pastures, bogs. Common, widespread.

CREICH   LAIRG   ROGART   DORNOCH   GOLSPIE   CLYNE   LOTH   KILDONAN
ASSYNT   EDDRACHILLIS   DURNESS   TONGUE   FARR

J. balticus Willd. (107, 108) Baltic Rush
Dune slacks. Occasional.
——   ——   ——   DORNOCH   GOLSPIE   ——   ——   ——
——   EDDRACHILLIS   DURNESS   TONGUE   FARR

J. acutiflorus Ehrh. ex Hoffm. (107, 108) Sharp-flowered Rush
Wet meadows, moors and woods. Frequent.
CREICH   ——   ——   DORNOCH   GOLSPIE   ——   ——   KILDONAN
ASSYNT   EDDRACHILLIS   DURNESS   TONGUE   FARR

J. articulatus L. (107, 108) Jointed Rush
Marshes, wet meadows. Common, widespread.
CREICH   LAIRG   ROGART   DORNOCH   GOLSPIE   CLYNE   LOTH   KILDONAN
ASSYNT   EDDRACHILLIS   DURNESS   TONGUE   FARR

J. alpinoarticulatus Chaix (108) Alpine Rush
Marshy places on mountains. Rare.

ASSYNT   ——   ——   TONGUE   ——
Assynt (Inchnadamph, 1887, E.S.M.)
Tongue (Ben Loyal, R.M.)

J. bulbosus L. (107, 108) Bulbous Rush
Wet bare places in heaths and woods. Common, widespread.
CREICH   LAIRG   ROGART   DORNOCH   GOLSPIE   CLYNE   LOTH   KILDONAN
ASSYNT   EDDRACHILLIS   DURNESS   TONGUE   FARR

J. kochii F. W. Schultz (107, 108)
Wet heathy places. Ascends to 2000 ft. Occasional in west.
——   LAIRG   ——   ——   ——   ——   ——   ——
ASSYNT   EDDRACHILLIS   DURNESS   ——   FARR

J. castaneus Sm. (107) Chestnut Rush
Marshes and springs. 2500 ft. Very rare.
CREICH   ——   ——   ——   ——   ——   ——   ——

Creich (Ben More Assynt, 1960, D.A.R.)

J. biglumis L. (107) Two-flowered Rush
Stony places on hills at 2500 ft. Very rare.
CREICH   ——   ——   ——   ——   ——   ——   ——

L

Creich (Ben More Assynt, 1960, D.A.R.)

J. triglumis L. (107, 108) Three-flowered Rush
Wet rock-ledges on mountains. Occasional.
CREICH ——— ——— ——— ——— ——— ——— ———
ASSYNT EDDRACHILLIS DURNESS ——— ———
Creich (Ben More Assynt, 1827, R.G., 1959, D.A.R.)
Assynt (Conival, 1886, A.G., 1890, E.S.M.)
Durness (Ben Hope, 1957, R.E.C.F.)

Luzula DC.

L. pilosa (L.) Willd. (107, 108) Hairy Wood-rush
Woods. Frequent in east, sparse in west.
CREICH LAIRG ROGART DORNOCH GOLSPIE CLYNE LOTH KILDONAN
ASSYNT ——— DURNESS TONGUE FARR

L. sylvatica (Huds.) Gaudin. (107, 108) Great Wood-rush
Woods, shady rocky places by streams. Common, widespread.
CREICH LAIRG ROGART DORNOCH GOLSPIE CLYNE LOTH KILDONAN
ASSYNT EDDRACHILLIS DURNESS TONGUE FARR

L. spicata (L.) DC. (107, 108) Spiked Wood-rush
Rocky ledges on many western hills. Occasional.
CREICH LAIRG ——— ——— ——— ——— ——— KILDONAN
ASSYNT EDDRACHILLIS DURNESS TONGUE FARR
Creich (Ben More Assynt)
Lairg (Ben Hee)
Kildonan (Ben Griam)

L. arcuata Sw. (107, 108) Curved Wood-rush
Stony ground on mountains, about 3000 ft. Very rare.
CREICH ——— ——— ——— ——— ——— ——— ———
——— ——— DURNESS ——— ———
Creich (Ben More Assynt, 1824, R.G., 1899, C.E.S.)
Durness (Foinaven, summit, 1824, R.G.)

L. campestris (L.) DC. (107, 108) Field Wood-rush
Grassy places. Common, widespread.
CREICH LAIRG ROGART DORNOCH GOLSPIE CLYNE LOTH KILDONAN
ASSYNT EDDRACHILLIS DURNESS TONGUE FARR

L. multiflora (Retz.) Lejeune (107, 108) Heath Wood-rush or
Many-headed Wood-rush
Heaths, woodland. Common, widespread.

152

CREICH LAIRG ROGART DORNOCH GOLSPIE CLYNE LOTH KILDONAN
ASSYNT EDDRACHILLIS DURNESS TONGUE FARR

AMARYLLIDACEAE
Allium L.

A. ursinum L. (107, 108) Ramsons or Garlic
Damp woods, shady places. Occasional.
—— LAIRG ROGART —— GOLSPIE —— ——
ASSYNT EDDRACHILLIS DURNESS TONGUE FARR

IRIDACEAE
Iris L.

I. pseudacorus L. (107, 108) Yellow Iris or Yellow Flag
Marshes, swamps, stream sides. Common.
CREICH LAIRG ROGART DORNOCH GOLSPIE CLYNE LOTH KILDONAN
ASSYNT EDDRACHILLIS DURNESS TONGUE FARR

Crocosmia Planch.

C. × crocosmiflora (Lemoine) N. E. Br. (107, 108) Montbretia
Introduced. Occasional.

—— —— —— —— GOLSPIE CLYNE —— KILDONAN
ASSYNT EDDRACHILLIS —— —— FARR

ORCHIDACEAE
Cephalanthera Rich.

C. longifolia (L.) Fritsch (108) Narrow-leaved or Long-leaved Helleborine
Woods. Rare.

ASSYNT —— —— —— —— —— —— ——
Assynt (Inverkirkaig & Lochinver)

Epipactis Sw.

E. helleborine (L.) Crantz. (108) Broad-leaved Helleborine
Woods. Rare.

ASSYNT —— —— —— TONGUE ——
Assynt (Achmelvich)
Tongue (Melness & Tongue)

E. atrorubens (Hoffm.) Schult. (108) Dark-red Helleborine

153

Limestone rocks and screes. Occasional.

| ASSYNT | — | — | DURNESS | TONGUE | FARR |

Assynt (*Inchnadamph*)
Durness (*Koeldale* & *Smoo*)
Tongue (*Melness*)
Farr (*Invernaver*)

Listera R. Br.

L. ovata (L.) R. Br. (107, 108) Common Twayblade
Damp sandy pastures. Frequent.

| CREICH | — | — | DORNOCH | — | — | — | KILDONAN |
| ASSYNT | EDDRACHILLIS | | DURNESS | TONGUE | FARR | | |

L. cordata (L.) R. Br. (107, 108) Lesser Twayblade
Pine woods and moorland under heather. Sparsely but widely distributed.
Frequent.

| CREICH | LAIRG | ROGART | DORNOCH | GOLSPIE | CLYNE | LOTH | KILDONAN |
| ASSYNT | EDDRACHILLIS | | DURNESS | TONGUE | FARR | | |

Goodyera R. Br.

G. repens (L.) R. Br. (107, 108) Creeping Lady's-tresses
Pine woods. Occasional.

| CREICH | — | — | DORNOCH | GOLSPIE | — | — | — |
| — | — | | — | TONGUE | — | — | |

Hammarbya Kuntze

H. paludosa (L.) Kuntze (107, 108) Bog Orchid
In wet moss on moors and in bogs. Rare.

| CREICH | LAIRG | — | — | — | — | — | KILDONAN |
| ASSYNT | EDDRACHILLIS | | DURNESS | TONGUE | — | | |

Creich (*Oykell Bridge, 1833, R.G., Shin Bridge, 1943, A.T.*)
Lairg (*Lairg, 1957, I.H.*)
Kildonan (*Torrish, 1962, M.McC.W.*)
Assynt (*Lochinver, 1890, E.S.M.*)
Eddrachillis (*Kylesku, 1943, A.T., Loch Stack, 1964, D.A.R.*)
Durness (*Eriboll*)
Tongue (*Scullomie, 1890, E.S.M., Ben Loyal, 1943, A.T.*)

Coeloglossum Hartm.

C. viride (L.) Hartm. (107, 108) Frog Orchid

154

Sandy pastures by the sea. Frequent.

| | | | DORNOCH | GOLSPIE | | | |
| ASSYNT | EDDRACHILLIS | | DURNESS | TONGUE | FARR | | |

Gymnadenia R. Br.

G. conopsea (L.) R. Br. (107, 108) Fragrant Orchid
sub sp. **conopsea**
Grassland and heaths. Frequent.

| CREICH | LAIRG | | DORNOCH | GOLSPIE | | LOTH | KILDONAN |
| ASSYNT | EDDRACHILLIS | | DURNESS | TONGUE | FARR | | |

Leucorchis E. Mey

L. albida (L.) E. Mey. ex schur (107, 108) Small white Orchid
Pastures. Frequent.

| CREICH | LAIRG | | | | | | |
| ASSYNT | EDDRACHILLIS | | DURNESS | TONGUE | FARR | | |

Platanthera Rich.

P. chlorantha (Custer) Reichb. (107, 108) Greater Butterfly-orchid
Wet pastures. Occasional.

| CREICH | LAIRG | | | | | | |
| ASSYNT | EDDRACHILLIS | | DURNESS | TONGUE | FARR | | |

P. bifolia (L.) Rich (107, 108) Lesser Butterfly-orchid
Wet pastures. Frequent.

| CREICH | LAIRG | ROGART | DORNOCH | GOLSPIE | CLYNE | | |
| ASSYNT | EDDRACHILLIS | | DURNESS | TONGUE | FARR | | |

Orchis L.

O. mascula (L.) L. (107, 108) Early-purple Orchid
Pastures. Frequent.

| | | ROGART | DORNOCH | | CLYNE | | |
| ASSYNT | EDDRACHILLIS | | DURNESS | TONGUE | FARR | | |

Dactylorchis (Klinge) Vermeul.

D. fuchsii (Druce) Vermeul. (107, 108) Common Spotted-orchid
Damp meadows. Frequent.

| | | ROGART | DORNOCH | GOLSPIE | | | |
| ASSYNT | EDDRACHILLIS | | DURNESS | TONGUE | FARR | | |

D. maculata (L.) Vermeul. (107, 108) Heath Spotted-orchid
Damp heaths and moors. Common, widespread.
CREICH LAIRG ROGART DORNOCH GOLSPIE CLYNE LOTH KILDONAN
ASSYNT EDDRACHILLIS DURNESS TONGUE FARR

D. incarnata (L.) Vermeul. (107, 108) Meadow Orchid or
Early Marsh-orchid
Marshes, damp pastures near the sea. Frequent.
CREICH LAIRG ROGART DORNOCH GOLSPIE CLYNE LOTH KILDONAN
ASSYNT EDDRACHILLIS DURNESS TONGUE FARR

D. purpurella (T. & T. A. Stephenson) Vermeul. (107, 108)
Northern Marsh-orchid or Dwarf Purple Orchid
Wet grassy places. Frequent.
CREICH LAIRG ROGART DORNOCH GOLSPIE CLYNE LOTH KILDONAN
ASSYNT EDDRACHILLIS DURNESS TONGUE FARR

D. kerryensis (Wilmott) P. F. Hunt & Summerhayes
Irish Marsh-orchid
sub sp. **occidentalis** (Pugsl.) P. F. Hunt & Summerhayes (108)
Marshes. Rare.

———   ———   ———   ———   ———   ———   FARR

Farr (*Melvich*)

LEMNACEAE
Lemna L.

L. minor L. (107) Common Duckweed
In ponds. Rare.
———   ———   ROGART DORNOCH ———   ———   LOTH ———

Rogart (*Rogart, 1959, M.McC.W.*)
Dornoch (*Dornoch, 1955, J.A.*)
Loth (*Glen Sletdale, 1962, V.S.S.*)

SPARGANIACEAE
Sparganium L.

S. erectum L. (107, 108) Branched Bur-reed
Lochans. Occasional.
———   ———   ROGART ———   GOLSPIE ———   KILDONAN
———   ———   DURNESS ———   FARR

S. emersum Rehm. (108) Unbranched Bur-reed

156

Lochans. Rare.

S. angustifolium Michx. (107, 108) Floating Bur-reed
Lochs. Occasional.

S. minimum Wallr. (107, 108) Least Bur-reed or Small Bur-reed
Lochans. Occasional.

TYPHACEAE
Typha L.

T. latifolia L. (107) Bulrush or Great Reedmace
In a pond. Rare.

Dornoch (Dornoch, 1955, J.A.)

CYPERACEAE
Eriophorum L.

E. angustifolium Honck. (107, 108) Common Cottongrass
Bog pools. Common, widespread.

E. latifolium Hoppe (107, 108) Broad-leaved Cottongrass
Wet places on basic soil. Occasional.

E. vaginatum L. (107, 108) Hare's-tail Cottongrass
Wet places on heaths and moors. Common, widespread.

Scirpus L.

S. caespitosus L. (107, 108) Deergrass
Wet heaths. Common, widespread.

CREICH LAIRG ROGART DORNOCH GOLSPIE CLYNE LOTH KILDONAN
ASSYNT EDDRACHILLIS DURNESS TONGUE FARR

S. lacustris L. (107, 108) Common Club-rush or Bulrush
Lochs. Occasional.
CREICH ——— ——— ——— ——— CLYNE ——— KILDONAN
ASSYNT EDDRACHILLIS ——— TONGUE FARR

S. setaceus L. (107, 108) Bristle Club-rush
Damp bare places. Frequent.
CREICH LAIRG ROGART DORNOCH GOLSPIE CLYNE LOTH KILDONAN
ASSYNT EDDRACHILLIS ——— TONGUE FARR

S. fluitans L. (108) Floating Club-rush or Floating Spike-rush
Marshes and lochans. Frequent near north and west coasts.

——— ——— ——— ——— ——— ——— ———
ASSYNT EDDRACHILLIS DURNESS TONGUE FARR

Eleocharis R. Br.

E. quinqueflora (F. X. Hartmann.) Schwarz (107, 108)
Few-flowered Spike-rush
Damp peaty places on moors. Common.
CREICH LAIRG ROGART DORNOCH GOLSPIE CLYNE ——— KILDONAN
ASSYNT EDDRACHILLIS DURNESS TONGUE FARR

E. multicaulis (Sm.) Sm. (107, 108) Many-stalked Spike-rush
Wet peaty places in bogs. Occasional.
CREICH LAIRG ——— ——— ——— ——— ——— ———
ASSYNT EDDRACHILLIS DURNESS TONGUE FARR

E. palustris (L.) Roem. & Schult. (107, 108) Common Spike-rush
Margins of lochs. Common.
CREICH LAIRG ROGART DORNOCH GOLSPIE CLYNE LOTH KILDONAN
ASSYNT EDDRACHILLIS DURNESS TONGUE FARR

E. uniglumis (Link) Schult. (107, 108) Slender Spike-rush
Marshes near the sea. Rare.
——— ——— ——— DORNOCH ——— ——— ———
ASSYNT EDDRACHILLIS ——— TONGUE FARR
Assynt (Inverkirkaig, Lochinver)
Eddrachillis (Laxford Bridge)
Tongue (Melness)
Farr (Invernaver, Altnaharra, Melvich)

158

Blysmus Panz.

B. rufus (Huds.) Link (107, 108) Narrow Blysmus or
Saltmarsh Flat-sedge
Grassy salt marshes. Frequent.

——— ——— ——— DORNOCH GOLSPIE ——— ——— ———
ASSYNT EDDRACHILLIS DURNESS TONGUE FARR

Schoenus L.

S. nigricans L. (107, 108) Black Bog-rush
Damp peaty places. Common.
CREICH LAIRG ROGART DORNOCH GOLSPIE CLYNE LOTH KILDONAN
ASSYNT EDDRACHILLIS DURNESS TONGUE FARR

Rhynchospora Vahl

R. alba (L.) Vahl (107, 108) White Beak-sedge
Wet peaty places. Occasional.
CREICH ——— ——— ——— ——— ——— KILDONAN
ASSYNT EDDRACHILLIS DURNESS TONGUE FARR

Cladium Browne

C. mariscus (L.) Pohl (108) Great Fen-sedge or Saw Sedge
In a peaty pool. Rare.

——— ——— ——— ——— ——— ——— ———
——— EDDRACHILLIS ——— ——— ———
Eddrachillis (between Kylestrome & Badcall)

Carex L.

C. laevigata Sm. (107, 108) Smooth-stalked Sedge
Marshes. Rare.

——— ——— ——— ——— ——— ——— ——— KILDONAN
——— EDDRACHILLIS ——— ——— ———
Eddrachillis (Loch Laxford, 1955, A.S., Handa Is., 1953, H.H.)
Kildonan (Kildonan, 1956, Torrish, 1962, M.McC.W.)

C. distans L. (108) Distant Sedge
Marshes near the sea. Rare.

——— ——— ——— ——— ——— ——— ———
——— EDDRACHILLIS DURNESS ——— FARR
Eddrachillis (Kinlochbervie, Sheigra, 1948, M.McC.W.)
Durness (Balnakeil, 1948, M.McC.W.)

159

Farr (*Invernaver, 1954, J.A.*)

C. hostiana DC. (107, 108) Tawny Sedge
Marshes, wet pastures and moors. Common.
CREICH LAIRG ROGART DORNOCH GOLSPIE CLYNE LOTH KILDONAN
ASSYNT EDDRACHILLIS DURNESS TONGUE FARR

C. binervis Sm. (107, 108) Green-ribbed Sedge
Heaths and moors. Common, widespread.
CREICH LAIRG ROGART DORNOCH GOLSPIE CLYNE LOTH KILDONAN
ASSYNT EDDRACHILLIS DURNESS TONGUE FARR

C. lepidocarpa Tausch (107, 108) Long-stalked Yellow Sedge
Wet heaths. Frequent.
—— —— —— —— —— —— —— KILDONAN
ASSYNT EDDRACHILLIS DURNESS TONGUE FARR

C. demissa Hornem (107, 108) Common Yellow Sedge
Stony places and grassland. Common, widespread.
CREICH LAIRG ROGART DORNOCH GOLSPIE CLYNE LOTH KILDONAN
ASSYNT EDDRACHILLIS DURNESS TONGUE FARR

C. scandinavica E. W. Davies (108) Northern Yellow Sedge
Rocky places. Rare.
—— —— —— —— —— —— ——
—— EDDRACHILLIS —— —— ——
Eddrachillis (*Sheigra & Sandwood, 1951, M.McC.W., Rhiconich, 1963, A.G.K.*)

C. serotina Mérat (107, 108) Small-fruited Yellow Sedge or
Dwarf Yellow Sedge
Damp sandy places. Occasional.
—— —— —— DORNOCH GOLSPIE —— —— KILDONAN
ASSYNT EDDRACHILLIS DURNESS TONGUE FARR

C. extensa Gooden. (107, 108) Long-bracted Sedge
Grassy salt marshes. Occasional.
—— —— —— DORNOCH —— —— ——
ASSYNT EDDRACHILLIS DURNESS TONGUE FARR

C. sylvatica Huds. (107, 108) Wood Sedge
Woods. Rare.
—— LAIRG ROGART —— —— —— ——
—— EDDRACHILLIS —— —— —— ——
Lairg (*Loch Shin*)

160

Rogart (Strath Fleet)
Eddrachillis (Kylesku)

C. capillaris L. (107, 108) Hair Sedge
Wet grassy places on basic soil. Mainly on north and west coast.
Frequent.

					KILDONAN
ASSYNT	EDDRACHILLIS	DURNESS	TONGUE	FARR	

C. rostrata Stokes (107, 108) Bottle Sedge
Margins of lochans and marshes. Common.

CREICH	LAIRG	ROGART	DORNOCH	GOLSPIE	CLYNE	LOTH	KILDONAN
ASSYNT	EDDRACHILLIS		DURNESS	TONGUE	FARR		

C. vesicaria L. (107) Bladder Sedge
Margins of lochs. Rare.

					CLYNE		KILDONAN

Clyne (Loch Brora, 1957, W.A.T.)
Kildonan (Kildonan, 1957, M.McC.W.)

C. saxatilis L. (107, 108) Russet Sedge
Mountain bogs. Rare.

CREICH							
					FARR		

Creich (Ben More Assynt at 2700 ft, 1960, D.A.R.)
Farr (Ben Klibreck, 1952, J.R.)

C. pallescens L. (107, 108) Pale Sedge
Wet woods. Frequent.

CREICH	LAIRG	ROGART	DORNOCH	GOLSPIE	CLYNE	LOTH	KILDONAN
ASSYNT	EDDRACHILLIS		DURNESS	TONGUE	FARR		

C. panicea L. (107, 108) Carnation Sedge
Wet grassy places. Common, widespread.

CREICH	LAIRG	ROGART	DORNOCH	GOLSPIE	CLYNE	LOTH	KILDONAN
ASSYNT	EDDRACHILLIS		DURNESS	TONGUE	FARR		

C. vaginata Tausch (108) Sheathed Sedge
Wet rocky places. Rare.

	EDDRACHILLIS	DURNESS					

Eddrachillis (Oldshoremore, 1833, W.H.C.)
Durness (Foinaven, 1957, E.A.B.)

C. limosa L. (107, 108) Bog Sedge or Mud Sedge
Muddy margins of lochans. Occasional.

CREICH —— ROGART —— —— —— —— ——
ASSYNT EDDRACHILLIS DURNESS TONGUE FARR

C. flacca Schreb. (107, 108) Glaucous Sedge or Carnation grass
Calcareous grassland. Common.

CREICH LAIRG ROGART DORNOCH GOLSPIE CLYNE LOTH KILDONAN
ASSYNT EDDRACHILLIS DURNESS TONGUE FARR

C. lasiocarpa Ehr. (107, 108) Slender Sedge
Swamps and loch margins. Occasional.

CREICH —— ROGART —— —— —— —— ——
ASSYNT EDDRACHILLIS DURNESS TONGUE FARR

C. pilulifera L. (107, 108) Pill Sedge
Grassy and heathy places. Common, widespread.

CREICH LAIRG ROGART DORNOCH GOLSPIE CLYNE LOTH KILDONAN
ASSYNT EDDRACHILLIS DURNESS TONGUE FARR

C. caryophyllea Latourr. (108) Spring Sedge
Calcareous pastures. Occasional.

—— —— —— —— —— —— —— ——
ASSYNT EDDRACHILLIS DURNESS —— FARR
Assynt (Hills round Inchnadamph)
Eddrachillis (Scourie, Rhiconich)
Farr (Invernaver)

C. acuta L. (108) Slender Tufted Sedge
In bog. Very rare.

—— —— —— —— —— —— —— ——
—— —— —— —— —— FARR
Farr (Altnaharra, 1963, C.R.L.)

C. aquatilis Wahlenb. (108) Water Sedge or Straight-leaved Sedge
Margins of streams. Rare.

—— —— —— —— —— —— —— ——
—— —— —— —— —— FARR
Farr (Altnaharra, 1882, H.E.F. & F.J.H., 1897, E.S.M. & W.A.S.,
1900, E.S.M., 1907 & 1915, G.C.D.)

C. recta Boott (107) Estuarine Sedge
On silt. Very rare.
Dornoch (Loch Fleet)

C. nigra (L.) Reichard (107, 108) Common Sedge
Wet grassy places. Common, widespread.
CREICH LAIRG ROGART DORNOCH GOLSPIE CLYNE LOTH KILDONAN
ASSYNT EDDRACHILLIS DURNESS TONGUE FARR

C. bigelowii Torr. ex Schwein. (107, 108) Stiff Sedge
Damp stony places on the higher hills. Frequent.
CREICH LAIRG —— —— —— —— KILDONAN
ASSYNT EDDRACHILLIS DURNESS TONGUE FARR

C. paniculata L. (108) Greater Tussock Sedge or Panicled Sedge
Wet grass. Rare.
—— —— —— —— —— —— ——
—— EDDRACHILLIS —— ——
Eddrachillis (Sandwood, 1948, M.McC.W., Handa, 1962, B.S.B., Eriboll, 1964, A.G.K.)

C. diandra Schrank (107) Lesser Tussock Sedge or Lesser Fox Sedge
In bog. Rare.
—— —— ROGART —— —— —— —— ——
—— —— —— —— —— —— ——
Rogart (Rogart, 1950, M.McC.W.)

C. disticha Huds. (107, 108) Brown Sedge
In wet grass. Rare.
CREICH —— —— —— —— —— ——
—— —— DURNESS —— ——
Creich (Invershin, 1907, G.C.D.)
Durness (Durness)

C. arenaria L. (107, 108) Sand Sedge
Sandy sea-shores. Frequent.
—— —— —— DORNOCH GOLSPIE CLYNE LOTH KILDONAN
ASSYNT EDDRACHILLIS DURNESS TONGUE FARR

C. chordorrhiza L. f. (108) String Sedge
In sphagnum bogs. Very rare.
—— —— —— —— —— —— —— ——
—— —— —— —— FARR
Farr (Altnaharra, 1897, E.S.M. & W.A.S., Mudale, 1907, G.C.D.)

C. maritima Gunn (107, 108) Curved Sedge
On sandy sea-shores. Occasional.
—— —— —— DORNOCH —— CLYNE —— ——
—— —— DURNESS TONGUE FARR

163

Dornoch (*Dornoch*)
Clyne (*Brora*)
Durness (*Koeldale*)
Tongue (*Scullomia, Melness*)
Farr (*Invernaver*)

C. echinata Murr. (107, 108) Star Sedge
Moors and bogs. Common, widespread.

CREICH LAIRG ROGART DORNOCH GOLSPIE CLYNE LOTH KILDONAN
ASSYNT EDDRACHILLIS DURNESS TONGUE FARR

C. remota L. (107, 108) Remote Sedge
Wet shady places. Rare.

—— —— —— DORNOCH —— CLYNE —— KILDONAN
ASSYNT —— —— —— ——
Dornoch (*Cambusmore, 1960, J.A.*)
Clyne (*Brora, 1958, M.McC.W.*)
Kildonan (*Suisgill, 1958, M.McC.W.*)
Assynt (*Lochinver, Stoer, 1944, A.J.W.*)

C. curta Gooden. (107, 108) White Sedge
Bogs and marshes. Frequent.

—— —— ROGART DORNOCH —— CLYNE —— KILDONAN
ASSYNT EDDRACHILLIS DURNESS TONGUE FARR

C. ovalis Gooden. (107, 108) Oval Sedge
Rough grassy and waste places. Common.

CREICH LAIRG ROGART DORNOCH GOLSPIE CLYNE LOTH KILDONAN
ASSYNT EDDRACHILLIS DURNESS TONGUE FARR

C. rupestris All. (108) Rock Sedge
Ledges on limestone rocks. From 50 ft on sea-cliffs to 1500 ft on hills
round Inchnadamph. Rare.

ASSYNT —— DURNESS ——
Assynt (*Inchnadamph, 1890, E.S.M., Knockan, 1895, G.C.D., 1960, J.A.*)
Durness (*Durness, 1865, I.B., Heilam Ferry & Smoo, 1960, D.A.R.*)

C. pauciflora Lightf. (107, 108) Few-flowered Sedge
In bogs. Frequent.

CREICH LAIRG —— —— —— —— —— KILDONAN
ASSYNT EDDRACHILLIS DURNESS TONGUE FARR

C. pulicaris L. (107, 108) Flea Sedge
In damp places. Common, widespread.

164

CREICH LAIRG ROGART DORNOCH GOLSPIE CLYNE LOTH KILDONAN
ASSYNT EDDRACHILLIS DURNESS TONGUE FARR

C. dioica L. (107, 108) Dioecious Sedge
On moors and bogs. Common.
CREICH LAIRG ROGART DORNOCH GOLSPIE CLYNE LOTH KILDONAN
ASSYNT EDDRACHILLIS DURNESS TONGUE FARR

GRAMINEAE
Phragmites Adans.

P. communis Trin. (107, 108) Common Reed
In swamps. Frequent.
CREICH LAIRG ROGART DORNOCH GOLSPIE CLYNE LOTH KILDONAN
ASSYNT EDDRACHILLIS DURNESS TONGUE FARR

Molinia Schrank

M. caerulea (L.) Moench (107, 108) Purple Moor-grass
Wet places on heaths and mountains. Common, widespread.
CREICH LAIRG ROGART DORNOCH GOLSPIE CLYNE LOTH KILDONAN
ASSYNT EDDRACHILLIS DURNESS TONGUE FARR

Sieglingia Bernh.

S. decumbens (L.) Bernh. (107, 108) Heath-grass
On peaty and sandy soils. Common, widespread.
CREICH LAIRG ROGART DORNOCH GOLSPIE CLYNE LOTH KILDONAN
ASSYNT EDDRACHILLIS DURNESS TONGUE FARR

Glyceria R. Br.

G. fluitans (L.) R. Br. (107, 108) Floating Sweet-grass or Flote-grass
In shallow water, ditches, ponds. Common.
CREICH LAIRG ROGART DORNOCH GOLSPIE CLYNE LOTH KILDONAN
ASSYNT EDDRACHILLIS DURNESS TONGUE FARR

G. plicata Fr. (107, 108) Plicate Sweet-grass
In ditches. Rare.
———— ———— ———— ———— ———— ———— ———— KILDONAN
———— EDDRACHILLIS ———— ———— ————
Kildonan (*Helmsdale*)
Eddrachillis (*Handa*)

G. declinata Bréb. (107) Small Sweet-grass or Glaucous Sweet-grass

In muddy pools. Rare.

—— —— —— —— —— —— LOTH ——

—— —— —— —— —— ——

Loth (Portgower)

G. maxima (Hartm.) Holmberg. (107) Reed Sweet-grass
Margins of streams. Rare.

—— —— —— DORNOCH —— —— —— ——

—— —— —— —— —— ——

Dornoch (Cambusmore)

Festuca L.

F. pratensis Huds. (107) Meadow Fescue
Damp meadows. Rare.

CREICH —— —— —— —— CLYNE —— KILDONAN

—— —— —— —— ——

F. arundinacea Schreb. (107, 108) Tall Fescue
Grassy places near the sea. Rare.

—— —— —— DORNOCH —— —— —— ——

—— —— —— —— FARR

F. rubra L. (107, 108) Red Fescue or Creeping Fescue
Grassland, heaths, dunes, salt-marshes. Common, widespread.

CREICH LAIRG ROGART DORNOCH GOLSPIE CLYNE LOTH KILDONAN
ASSYNT EDDRACHILLIS DURNESS TONGUE FARR

F. ovina L. (107, 108) Sheep's-fescue
Grassy places. Common, widespread.

CREICH LAIRG ROGART DORNOCH GOLSPIE CLYNE LOTH KILDONAN
ASSYNT EDDRACHILLIS DURNESS TONGUE FARR

F. tenuifolia Sibth. (107, 108) Fine-leaved Sheep's-fescue
Grassy places. Common.

CREICH LAIRG —— —— —— CLYNE —— KILDONAN
ASSYNT —— —— TONGUE FARR

F. vivipara (L.) Sm. (107, 108) Viviparous Fescue
Pastures on mountains. At sea-level on north coast. Common.

CREICH LAIRG ROGART DORNOCH GOLSPIE CLYNE LOTH KILDONAN
ASSYNT EDDRACHILLIS DURNESS TONGUE FARR

Lolium L.

L. perenne L. (107, 108) Perennial Rye-grass

166

Grassy and waste places. Common.

CREICH LAIRG ROGART DORNOCH GOLSPIE CLYNE LOTH KILDONAN
ASSYNT EDDRACHILLIS DURNESS TONGUE FARR

L. multiflorum Lam. (107, 108) Italian Rye-grass
Fields and waysides. Frequent.

CREICH LAIRG ROGART DORNOCH GOLSPIE CLYNE LOTH KILDONAN
ASSYNT EDDRACHILLIS DURNESS TONGUE FARR

Vulpia C. C. Gmel.

V. bromoides (L.) Gray (107, 108) Barren Fescue or Squirreltail Fescue
Waste places, heaths. Occasional.

CREICH —— —— DORNOCH GOLSPIE —— —— KILDONAN
ASSYNT —— —— TONGUE FARR

V. myuros (L.) C. C. Gmel. (107) Rat's-tail Fescue
Casual.
Rogart (Rogart, 1961, M.McC.W.)

Puccinellia Parl.

P. maritima (Huds.) Parl. (107, 108) Common Saltmarsh-grass or
Sea Poa
Salt-marshes. Occasional.

—— —— —— DORNOCH GOLSPIE —— —— ——
—— —— DURNESS —— FARR

P. distans (L.) Parl. (108) Reflexed Poa or Reflexed Saltmarsh-grass
Salt marsh. Rare.

—— —— —— —— —— —— —— ——
—— —— DURNESS —— FARR
Durness (Durness, D.McC., 1966)

Catapodium Link

C. marinum (L.) C. E. Hubbard (108) Darnel Poa or Sea Fern-grass
Sea-shore. Rare.

—— —— —— —— —— —— —— ——
ASSYNT EDDRACHILLIS —— —— ——
Assynt (Clachtoll, 1944, A.J.W., 1966, M.McC.W.)
Eddrachillis (Pollin, 1956, M.McC.W.)

Poa L.

P. annua L. (107, 108) Annual Meadow-grass

167

Fields, roadsides, waste places. Common, widespread.

CREICH LAIRG ROGART DORNOCH GOLSPIE CLYNE LOTH KILDONAN
ASSYNT EDDRACHILLIS DURNESS TONGUE FARR

P. alpina L. (107) Alpine Meadow-grass
Stony places on mountains at 2500 ft. Rare.

CREICH —— —— —— —— ——
—— —— —— —— —— ——

Creich (Ben More Assynt, 1826, R.G., 1959, D.A.R.)

P. nemoralis L. (107, 108) Wood Meadow-grass
Woodlands. Occasional.

CREICH —— —— DORNOCH GOLSPIE —— LOTH KILDONAN
ASSYNT —— —— ——

P. glauca Vahl (108) Glaucous Meadow-grass
Damp rock ledges on hill to 2000 ft. Rare.

—— —— —— —— —— —— ——
ASSYNT —— DURNESS TONGUE ——
Assynt (Canisp, 1900, C.E.S.)
Durness (Meall Horn, 1958, D.A.R.)
Tongue (Ben Loyal, 1959, R.E.C.F.)

P. pratensis L. (107, 108) Smooth Meadow-grass
Pastures, roadsides, waste places. Common.

CREICH LAIRG ROGART DORNOCH GOLSPIE CLYNE LOTH KILDONAN
ASSYNT EDDRACHILLIS DURNESS TONGUE FARR

P. subcaerulea Sm. (107, 108) Spreading Meadow-grass
Damp coastal sand. Frequent.

—— —— —— DORNOCH GOLSPIE CLYNE LOTH ——
ASSYNT EDDRACHILLIS DURNESS TONGUE FARR

P. trivialis L. (107, 108) Rough Meadow-grass
Grassy places and waste land. Frequent.

CREICH LAIRG ROGART DORNOCH GOLSPIE CLYNE LOTH KILDONAN
ASSYNT EDDRACHILLIS DURNESS TONGUE FARR

Catabrosa Beauv.

C. aquatica (L.) Beauv. (107, 108) Whorl-grass or Water Whorl-grass
In shallow water. Rare.

—— —— —— DORNOCH —— —— ——
ASSYNT EDDRACHILLIS —— —— FARR
Dornoch (Mound, 1888, J.G., 1962, A.McG.S.)

168

Assynt (Clachtoll, 1886, A.G., 1957, B.F.)
Eddrachillis (Scourie, 1938, J.W.H.-H. & H.H.-H.)
Farr (Melvich)

Dactylis L.

D. glomerata L. (107, 108) Cock's-foot
Pastures, rough grassland, roadsides. Common.
CREICH   LAIRG   ROGART   DORNOCH   GOLSPIE   CLYNE   LOTH   KILDONAN
ASSYNT   EDDRACHILLIS   DURNESS   TONGUE   FARR

Cynosurus L.

C. cristatus L. (107, 108) Crested Dog's-tail
Grasslands. Common, widespread.
CREICH   LAIRG   ROGART   DORNOCH   GOLSPIE   CLYNE   LOTH   KILDONAN
ASSYNT   EDDRACHILLIS   DURNESS   TONGUE   FARR

Briza L.

B. media L. (107, 108) Quaking-grass
Grasslands. Rare.

				GOLSPIE			
ASSYNT	—		DURNESS	—		

Golspie (Dunrobin)
Assynt (Lochinver, Inchnadamph)
Durness (Durness)

Melica L.

M. uniflora Retz. (107) Wood Melick
Damp woods. Rare.

			DORNOCH	GOLSPIE			

Dornoch (Cambusmore)
Golspie (Golspie)

M. nutans L. (107, 108) Mountain Melick
Woods. Rare.

CREICH	—	—	DORNOCH	GOLSPIE	—	—	—
ASSYNT	—						

Creich (Invershin)
Dornoch (Cambusmore)
Golspie (Golspie)
Assynt (Lochinver, Inchnadamph)

Bromus L.

B. ramosus Huds. (107, 108) Hairy Brome
Woods. Occasional.

				GOLSPIE			
ASSYNT							

Golspie (Dunrobin)
Assynt (Lochinver, Inchnadamph)

B. sterilis L. (107, 108) Barren Brome
Waste places. Rare.

				GOLSPIE			KILDONAN
ASSYNT							

Golspie (Dunrobin)
Kildonan (Helmsdale)
Assynt (Inchnadamph)

B. mollis L. (107, 108) Lop-grass or Soft Brome
Fields, dunes, roadsides and waste places. Frequent.

CREICH	LAIRG	ROGART	DORNOCH	GOLSPIE	CLYNE	LOTH	KILDONAN
ASSYNT	EDDRACHILLIS		DURNESS	TONGUE	FARR		

B. thominii Hardouin. (107, 108) Lesser Soft Brome
Roadsides and waste places. Occasional.

	LAIRG		DORNOCH		CLYNE		KILDONAN
				TONGUE			

Lairg (Lairg)
Dornoch (Loch Fleet)
Clyne (Brora)
Kildonan (Borrobal)
Tongue (Melness, Scullomie)

B. lepidus Holmberg. (107, 108) Slender Soft Brome
Fields and roadsides. Frequent.

CREICH	LAIRG	ROGART	DORNOCH	GOLSPIE	CLYNE	LOTH	KILDONAN
	EDDRACHILLIS		DURNESS	TONGUE	FARR		

B. commutatus Schrad. (107, 108) Meadow Brome
Grassland. Rare.

CREICH				GOLSPIE			
ASSYNT							

Creich (Bonar Bridge)
Golspie (Golspie)
Assynt (Knockan)

170

Brachypodium Beauv.

B. sylvaticum (Huds.) Beauv. (107, 108) False Brome
Woods. Frequent.
CREICH LAIRG ROGART DORNOCH GOLSPIE ⸺ ⸺ ⸺
ASSYNT EDDRACHILLIS DURNESS TONGUE FARR

Agropyron Gaertn.

A. caninum (L.) Beauv. (107, 108) Bearded Couch
Damp woods. Rare.
⸺ ⸺ ⸺ DORNOCH GOLSPIE ⸺ ⸺ ⸺
ASSYNT ⸺ DURNESS TONGUE FARR

A. donianum F. B. White (107, 108) Don's Twitch or Don's Couch
Limestone rocks. Very rare.
⸺ ⸺ ⸺ DORNOCH ⸺ ⸺ ⸺ ⸺
ASSYNT ⸺ ⸺ ⸺ ⸺
Dornoch (Cambusmore)
Assynt (Inchnadamph)

A. repens (L.) Beauv. (107, 108) Common Couch
Cultivated fields and waste places. Frequent.
CREICH LAIRG ROGART DORNOCH GOLSPIE CLYNE LOTH KILDONAN
ASSYNT EDDRACHILLIS DURNESS TONGUE FARR

A. junceiforme (A. & D. Löve) A. & D. Löve (107, 108) Sand Couch
On sandy shores and dunes. Frequent.
⸺ ⸺ ⸺ DORNOCH GOLSPIE ⸺ ⸺ KILDONAN
ASSYNT EDDRACHILLIS DURNESS TONGUE FARR

Elymus L.

E. arenarius L. (107, 108) Lyme-grass
Seaward side of dunes. Occasional.
⸺ ⸺ ⸺ DORNOCH GOLSPIE ⸺ ⸺ KILDONAN
ASSYNT EDDRACHILLIS DURNESS TONGUE FARR

Hordeum L.

H. murinum L. (107) Wall Barley
Waste places. Very rare.
⸺ ⸺ ⸺ ⸺ ⸺ ⸺ ⸺ KILDONAN
⸺ ⸺ ⸺ ⸺ ⸺
Kildonan (Helmsdale)

171

Koeleria Pers.

K. cristata (L.) Pers. (107, 108) Crested Hair-grass
Coastal pastures. Frequent.

—   —   —   DORNOCH GOLSPIE CLYNE LOTH   KILDONAN
ASSYNT EDDRACHILLIS DURNESS TONGUE FARR

Trisetum Pers.

T. flavescens (L.) Beauv. (107, 108) Yellow Oat-grass
Grassy places. Rare.

—   —   —   —   —   CLYNE —   —
ASSYNT —   —   —   FARR
Assynt (Lochinver, 1886, A.G.)
Clyne (Brora, 1962, M.McC.W.)
Farr (Bettyhill, 1973, K.D.L.)

Avena L.

A. fatua L. (107, 108) Wild-oat
Fields. Rare.

—   —   ROGART —   —   —   —   —
—   —   —   TONGUE
Rogart (Rogart, 1957, M.McC.W.)
Tongue (Coldbackie, 1901, E.S.M.)

A. strigosa Schreb. (107) Bristle Oat or Black Oat
Creich (Bonar Bridge, 1836, A. Murray)

Helictotrichon Bess.

H. pratense (L.) Pilg. (107, 108) Meadow Oat-grass
Coastal turf. Rare.

—   —   —   GOLSPIE —   —   KILDONAN
—   EDDRACHILLIS DURNESS —   —

H. pubescens (Huds.) Pilg. (107, 108) Downy Oat-grass or
Hairy Oat-grass
Rough grassland. Frequent.
CREICH LAIRG ROGART DORNOCH GOLSPIE CLYNE LOTH   KILDONAN
ASSYNT EDDRACHILLIS DURNESS TONGUE FARR

Arrhenatherum Beauv.

A. elatius (L.) Beauv. ex J. & C. Presl. (107, 108) False Oat-grass

Roadsides and waste ground. Frequent.

CREICH LAIRG ROGART DORNOCH GOLSPIE CLYNE LOTH KILDONAN
ASSYNT EDDRACHILLIS DURNESS TONGUE FARR

Holcus L.

H. lanatus L. (107, 108) Yorkshire Fog
Rough grassland, waste places. Common, widespread.

CREICH LAIRG ROGART DORNOCH GOLSPIE CLYNE LOTH KILDONAN
ASSYNT EDDRACHILLIS DURNESS TONGUE FARR

H. mollis L. (107, 108) Creeping Soft-grass
Open woodlands. Common.

CREICH LAIRG ROGART DORNOCH GOLSPIE CLYNE LOTH KILDONAN
ASSYNT EDDRACHILLIS DURNESS TONGUE FARR

Deschampsia Beauv.

D. caespitosa (L.) Beauv. (107, 108) Tufted Hair-grass
Marshy fields, moors and woods. Common, widespread.

CREICH LAIRG ROGART DORNOCH GOLSPIE CLYNE LOTH KILDONAN
ASSYNT EDDRACHILLIS DURNESS TONGUE FARR

D. alpina (L.) Roem. & Schult. (107, 108) Alpine Hair-grass
Stony places on mountains from 2000 to 3000 ft. Rare.

CREICH —— —— —— ——
—— —— DURNESS —— ——
Creich (Ben More Assynt, 1824, R.G., 1897, E.S.M., 1962, D.A.R.)
Durness (Foinaven, summit, 1824, R.G.)

D. flexuosa (L.) Trin. (107, 108) Wavy Hair-grass
Heaths and moors. To 3000 ft. Common, widespread.

CREICH LAIRG ROGART DORNOCH GOLSPIE CLYNE LOTH KILDONAN
ASSYNT EDDRACHILLIS DURNESS TONGUE FARR

D. setacea (Huds.) Hack. (107, 108) Bog Hair-grass
Margins of peaty pools. Rare.

CREICH —— —— —— ——
—— EDDRACHILLIS —— TONGUE FARR
Creich (Invershin)
Eddrachillis (Sandwood)
Tongue (Tongue)
Farr (Altnaharra, Invernaver, Melvich)

173

Aira L.

A. praecox L. (107, 108) Early Hair-grass
On dry bare sandy and rocky slopes. Common, widespread.
CREICH LAIRG ROGART DORNOCH GOLSPIE CLYNE LOTH KILDONAN
ASSYNT EDDRACHILLIS DURNESS TONGUE FARR

A. caryophyllea L. (107, 108) Silver Hair-grass
Dry sandy soil on heaths and fields. Common.
CREICH LAIRG ROGART DORNOCH GOLSPIE CLYNE LOTH KILDONAN
ASSYNT EDDRACHILLIS DURNESS TONGUE FARR

Ammophila Host

A. arenaria (L.) Link (107, 108) Marram Grass
Coastal dunes. Frequent.
———— ———— ———— DORNOCH GOLSPIE CLYNE LOTH KILDONAN
ASSYNT EDDRACHILLIS DURNESS TONGUE FARR

× Ammocalamagrostis P. Fourn.

×**A. baltica** (Schrad.) P. Fourn. (108)
On dunes. Rare.
Eddrachillis (Handa Island, 1938, J.W.H.-H. & H.H.-H.)

Calamagrostis Adans.

C. epigejos (L.) Roth (108) Wood Small-reed or Bushgrass
Damp woods, ditches. Rare.
———— ———— ———— ———— ———— ———— ———— ————
ASSYNT EDDRACHILLIS ———— ———— ————
Assynt (Stoer, Oldany)
Eddrachillis (Handa Island)

Agrostis L.

A. canina L. (107, 108) Brown Bent-grass
Wet meadows, heaths, grassland on hills. Common.
CREICH LAIRG ROGART DORNOCH GOLSPIE CLYNE LOTH KILDONAN
ASSYNT EDDRACHILLIS DURNESS TONGUE FARR

A. tenuis Sibth. (107, 108) Common Bent-grass
On heaths, moors, waste ground. Common, widespread.
CREICH LAIRG ROGART DORNOCH GOLSPIE CLYNE LOTH KILDONAN
ASSYNT EDDRACHILLIS DURNESS TONGUE FARR

174

A. gigantea Roth (107, 108) Common Bent-grass or Black Bent-grass
Fields and roadsides. Rare.

| —— | —— | —— | DORNOCH | —— | —— | —— | KILDONAN |
| —— | —— | | —— | —— | FARR | | |

A. stolonifera L. (107, 108) Fiorin or Creeping Bent-grass
Grassland, coastal sands, salt-marsh. Frequent.

| CREICH | LAIRG | ROGART | DORNOCH | GOLSPIE | CLYNE | LOTH | KILDONAN |
| ASSYNT | EDDRACHILLIS | | DURNESS | TONGUE | FARR | | |

Phleum L.

P. bertolonii DC. (107, 108) Smaller Cat's-tail
Grassland. Probably overlooked.

| —— | —— | —— | —— | GOLSPIE | —— | —— | KILDONAN |
| ASSYNT | —— | | —— | —— | FARR | | |

P. pratense L. (107, 108) Timothy
Fields, roadsides. Occasional.

| CREICH | —— | —— | DORNOCH | GOLSPIE | —— | —— | KILDONAN |
| ASSYNT | EDDRACHILLIS | | DURNESS | TONGUE | FARR | | |

Alopecurus L.

A. myosuroides Huds. (108) Black Twitch or Black-grass
An old record.
Farr (Bettyhill, 1889, F.J.H. & J.C.M.)

A. pratensis L. (107, 108) Meadow Foxtail
Grassland. Frequent.

| CREICH | LAIRG | ROGART | DORNOCH | GOLSPIE | CLYNE | LOTH | KILDONAN |
| ASSYNT | EDDRACHILLIS | | DURNESS | TONGUE | FARR | | |

A. geniculatus L. (107, 108) Marsh Foxtail
Muddy margins of pools and ditches. Frequent.

| CREICH | LAIRG | ROGART | DORNOCH | GOLSPIE | CLYNE | LOTH | KILDONAN |
| ASSYNT | EDDRACHILLIS | | DURNESS | TONGUE | FARR | | |

A. bulbosus Gouan (108) Tuberous Foxtail or Bulbous Foxtail
Marshes. Rare.
Farr (Altnaharra, 1931, T.J.F.)

Milium L.

M. effusum L. (107) Wood Millet

Woodlands. Rare.

—— —— —— —— GOLSPIE —— —— ——

Golspie (*Dunrobin, 1897, E.S.M.*)

Anthoxanthum L.

A. odoratum L. (107, 108) Sweet Vernal-grass
Heaths, moors, grasslands. Common, widespread.
CREICH LAIRG ROGART DORNOCH GOLSPIE CLYNE LOTH KILDONAN
ASSYNT EDDRACHILLIS DURNESS TONGUE FARR

Phalaris L.

P. arundinacea L. (107, 108) Reed Canary-grass
Marshes, ditches, margins of ponds. Frequent.
CREICH LAIRG ROGART DORNOCH GOLSPIE CLYNE LOTH KILDONAN
ASSYNT EDDRACHILLIS DURNESS TONGUE FARR

P. canariensis L. (108) Canary-grass
Casual.
Durness (*Durness*)

Nardus L.

N. stricta L. (107, 108) Mat-grass
Heaths, moors, hill pastures. Common, widespread.
CREICH LAIRG ROGART DORNOCH GOLSPIE CLYNE LOTH KILDONAN
ASSYNT EDDRACHILLIS DURNESS TONGUE FARR

Index of english names

Bold figures indicate definitive references in the County Flora

180

N

N*

Index of latin names

Bold figures indicate definitive references in the County Flora

189

190

Carex L.,—*contd.*
  capillaris L., **161**
  caryophyllea Latour., **162**
  chordorrhiza L. f., 20, 24, 40, **163**
  curta Good., 16, **164**
  demissa Hornem., 30, **160**
  diandra Schrank, **163**
  dioica L., **165**
  distans L., **159**
  disticha Huds., **163**
  echinata Murr., 19, **164**
  extensa Gooden., **160**
  flacca Schreb., 19, 28, **162**
  hostiana DC., **160**
  laevigata Sm., **159**
  lasiocarpa Ehrh., **162**
  lepidocarpa Tausch, **160**
  limosa L., **162**
  maritima Gunn., 16, 20, 22, **163**
  nigra (L.) Reichard, **163**
  ovalis Good., **164**
  pallescens L., **161**
  panicea L., 30, **161**
  paniculata L., **163**
  pauciflora Lightf., 40, **164**
  pilulifera L., **162**
  pulicaris L., 19, **164**
  recta Boott, **162**
  remota L., 16, **164**
  rostrata Stokes, **161**
  rupestris All., 18, 19, 29, **164**
  saxatilis L., 25, **161**
  scandinavica E. W. Davies, **160**
  serotina Mérat, **160**
  sylvatica Huds., **160**
  vaginata Tausch, **161**
  vesicaria L., **161**
Carpinus L.
  betulus L., **103**
Carum L.
  carvi L., **97**
Castanea Mill.
  sativa Mill., **103**
Catabrosa Beauv.
  aquatica (L.) Beauv., 23, **168**
Catapodium Link
  marinum (L.) C. E. Hubbard, 24, **167**
Centaurea L.
  cyanus L., 17, **135**
  nigra L., **135**
  scabiosa L., 20, 21, 41, **134**
Centaurium Hill
  littorale (D. Turner) Gilmour, 16, **111**
Cephalanthera Rich.
  longifolia (L.) Fritsch, 24, **153**

Cerastium L.
  alpinum L., 13, 17, **66**
  arcticum Lange, **66**
  arvense L., **65**
  atrovirens Bab., **66**
  fontanum Baumg., **66**
  glomeratum Thuill., **66**
  holosteoides Fr., **66**
  semidecandrum L., **66**
  tomentosum L., **66**
Chamaenerion Adans.
  angustifolium (L.) Scop., **94**
Chamaepericlymenum Hill
  suecicum (L.) Aschers. & Graebn., 17,
    20, **95**
Chelidonium L.
  majus L., **56**
Chenopodium L.
  album L., **71**
  bonus-henricus L., 23, **70**
  rubrum L., **71**
Cherleria L.
  sedoides L., 19, 25, **68**
Chrysanthemum L.
  leucanthemum L., **133**
  parthenium (L.) Bernh., **133**
  segetum L., **133**
  vulgare (L.) Bernh., **133**
Chrysosplenium L.
  oppositifolium L., 22, **91**
Circaea L.
  ×intermedia Ehrh., **94**
  lutetiana L., **94**
Cirsium Mill.
  arvense (L.) Scop., **134**
  heterophyllum (L.) Hill, **134**
  palustre (L.) Scop., **134**
  vulgare (Savi) Ten., **134**
Cladium P. Br.
  mariscus (L.) Pohl, 22, **159**
Cochlearia L.
  alpina (Bab.) Hooker, **59**
  danica L., **59**
  officinalis L., 20, 31, **59**
  scotica Druce, 23, **59**
Coeloglossum Hartm.
  viride (L.) Hartm., 16, 20, 22, **154**
Conium L.
  maculatum L., 18, 22, **97**
Conopodium Koch
  majus (Gouan) Loret, **97**
Convolvulus L.
  arvensis L., **113**
Corydalis Vent.
  claviculata (L.) DC., 17, **56**

193